by John M. Carroll

Careers and Opportunities in Electronics
The Story of the Laser

THE STORY OF THE LASER

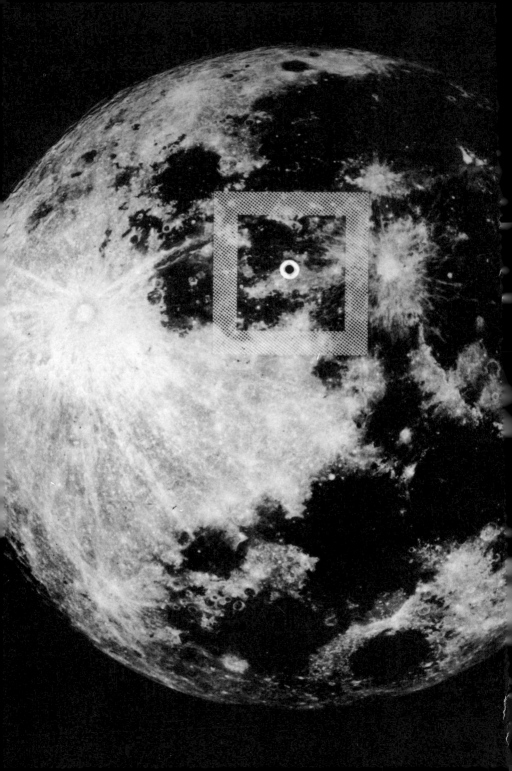

THE STORY OF
the laser

by John M. Carroll
Managing Editor, *Electronics* Magazine

NEW YORK
E. P. Dutton & Co., Inc.
1964

To Jack,
Bill, and Rob

PREFACE

In scientific research and development the gestation period between the conception of a new technology and its birth can range up to four years or even longer. This was not true of the laser.

Immediately after the announcement of the first laser in 1960, practically every company of any consequence in the electronics and aerospace industries—not to mention universities, government agencies, and research foundations—plunged into laser research.

In fiscal 1963, military spending for laser research and development exceeded $19 million. And 127 separate projects were under way. At least three of these were funded at a million dollars or more, and all of them had to do with the development of high-powered lasers for missile tracking and possible destruction. But most of the contracts ranged between $50,000 and $200,000.

Pursuing the study of the laser in all its infinite variety is an undertaking to challenge man's intellect and stretch his imagination. Here is a device that may profoundly change our daily lives. It is possible that the laser could make our continent safe from intercontinental ballistic missiles, help sweep the seas of prowling submarines, cure types of cancer, aid in designing computers that duplicate the human brain, magnify the capacity of our overburdened communications channels, and remodel the very foundations of life itself.

Today the laser is still in its infancy. It has proved successful in certain communications experiments and in tracking and ranging tests. Practical applications thus far include range finders for the Army, instruments for performing delicate eye operations, and apparatus for highly precise machining and welding.

Flamboyant public demonstrations of laser light beams piercing razor blades, popping toy balloons, and heating balls of steel wool to incandescence have given a carnival atmosphere to a serious scientific investigation, and left many people with the impression that the laser is just a high-priced toy.

The laser is not a toy. Nor is it a quick and easy answer to all man's technological problems. Rather it represents a significant scientific breakthrough that has greatly extended man's intellectual horizon. It represents a challenge to further scientific research and to sound engineering development.

This book explains in nontechnical language what the laser is and how it works. It traces the history of the laser from the first attempts to link the phenomena of light and electricity, one hundred years ago, to the scientific and engineering efforts of today. It explores the more important uses of the laser, both actual and potential, in national defense, space exploration, communications, data processing, medicine, and manufacturing. And it describes in detail the construction and operation of a simple laser—along with the safety precautions that must be observed.

The author thanks the members of the staff of *Electronics* magazine whose work makes this book possible, and especially W. W. MacDonald, editor, who granted permission to use photographs and drawings that first appeared in *Electronics*. Thanks are also due to many friends in industry who made information and material available: especially the Raytheon Company, Hughes Aircraft Company, and Perkin-Elmer Corporation.

JOHN MILLAR CARROLL

CONTENTS

	Preface	9
I	The Laser—What It Is and Does	17
II	What Led to the Invention	60
III	Lasers in War and Peace	102
IV	Construction of a Laser	146
	Conclusion	169
	Bibliography	171
	Index	177

ILLUSTRATIONS

Laser beam on moon compared with area of radar
    beam   19
Electromagnetic spectrum from radio frequencies to
    X rays   22
Frequency coherent and frequency incoherent
    radiation   26
Spatially coherent and spatially incoherent radiation   28
Exploded view of ruby laser showing ruby, mirrors,
    and helical flashtube   29
Energy level transitions in a ruby laser   31
How a ruby laser works   33-34
Helium-neon gas laser   36
Energy levels in a helium-neon laser   38
Semiconductor injection laser   41
Hertz's first radio transmitter and receiver   61
Black-body radiation curves showing variation in
    energy with frequency   65
Charles H. Townes, inventor of the maser, and Ali
    Javan, inventor of the gas laser   75
Energy levels in the two-level ammonia-beam maser,
    and configurations of the ammonia molecule   78
Nicolaas Bloembergen, father of the solid-state
    maser   83
James W. Meyer, inventor of the solid-state maser
    amplifier   85
Solid-state maser amplifier   86

Fifty-foot radio telescope atop Naval Research
    Laboratory uses a maser amplifier 89
Arthur L. Schawlow and medical team conducting
    ophthalmic laser experiment 93
Theodore H. Maiman, inventor of the ruby laser 94
Robert H. Rediker, Marshall I. Nathan, and Robert
    N. Hall, inventors of the injection laser 99
Proposed laser defense system against
    intercontinental ballistic missiles 107
Beam from a 500-joule laser blasts through a steel
    girder 112
Rifle-like laser range finder 122
Laser gyroscope 129
Laser piercing a sapphire crystal 131
Using a laser beam to read data from an automatic
    digital computer 135
Experimental setup for transmitting television sound
    and pictures over a laser beam 138
Pulling a calcium-tungstate crystal doped with
    neodymium out of a melt 150
Main parts of a ruby laser using a helical flash lamp 153
Laser-head designs used in optical pumping of ruby
    crystals 154
Typical laser system 158
Modern small laser and a portable power supply 167

THE STORY OF THE LASER

I

THE LASER—WHAT IT IS AND DOES

INTRODUCTION

In 1960, electronics scientists and engineers began to see things in a different light.

It was a rich ruby light: not "kindled in the vine," as the Persian poet Omar Khayyám said, but emitted by the atoms of a synthetic gem stone.

The light came from the laser, a new device with wide potential application in science, medicine, industry, and national defense.

WHAT'S IN A NAME?

The word laser is an acronym, or a word made up of the first letters of several other words. Laser stands for *L*ight *A*mplification by *S*timulated *E*mission of *R*adiation. It was coined by analogy with another acronym: *maser*. Maser stands for *M*icrowave *A*mplification by *S*timulated *E*mission of *R*adiation.

The maser works on the same basic principle as the laser but, of course, emits microwave energy rather than light. Masers are used as input amplifiers (preamplifiers) of radio telescopes and space-tracking receivers that magnify feeble signals gleaned from outer space.

No one is completely satisfied with the name "laser" because lasers do not really amplify light in a strict sense;

17

instead they generate light with particular characteristics that engineers and scientists find useful. In electronics terminology a device that generates radiation is called an oscillator, not an amplifier.

Furthermore, most lasers do not emit visible light at all but rather infrared, or invisible, light. It is conceivable that devices working on the same principle as the laser and maser may someday emit ultraviolet or so-called black light, X rays, or even gamma rays.

Scientists who moved from maser research into laser research insist on calling the laser an optical maser. But it can be argued that it is ridiculous to talk of "optical microwave amplification by stimulated emission of radiation" since "optical" means one thing and "microwave" quite another.

Proponents of the term "optical maser" counter by saying that "maser" doesn't stand for microwave amplification by stimulated emission of radiation at all, but rather for *molecular* amplification by stimulated emission of radiation.

To the comment that masers do not amplify molecules comes the answer that they depend for their action on the behavior of the molecules of the substance.

Well, *some* masers and lasers do depend on molecular effects. But more depend on the behavior of submolecular particles: atoms, ions (atoms that have lost one or more electrons), perhaps even electrons themselves.

Recently the term *quantum device* has been applied to both masers and lasers, and this seems to make sense, since the action of both the laser and the maser can be explained by the science of *quantum mechanics*. In fact, some scientists and engineers interested in lasers and masers are attempting to form within the Institute of Electrical and Electronics Engineers a professional group on quantum electronics. And though for the present the term "laser" seems deeply ingrained in the scientific vocabulary, let's remember that the science we call electronics was once known as thermionic engineering!

WHAT'S SPECIAL ABOUT A LASER?

The important thing about laser light is that it is coherent. The individual light rays are all of the same wavelength or color, and are all in step. A laser beam differs from a beam of ordinary light in both character and effectiveness in the same way that a platoon of well-drilled soldiers differs from a ragtag, disorganized mob.

When light waves from a laser march in step, they can perform amazing feats. The reason is that their energy is not dissipated as the beam spreads out. This makes for an intense concentration of energy at a very sharply defined point. It also greatly extends the range of a light source.

Three of the many spectacular achievements of the laser demonstrate how the properties of coherent light can be put to work:

• Because its light does not spread out even at great distances, a laser can illuminate the surface of the moon with a two-mile-wide circle of light.

Laser beam on moon (black dot) compared with area of radar beam (shaded area) (Raytheon)

• Because its energy is concentrated at a fine point, it can send a short, searing pinpoint of light into the human eyeball to weld a detached retina back into place and restore sight.

• And since its radiation is so intense, it can burn holes in a steel plate ⅛ inch thick at a distance of several feet.

These abilities have given rise to a whole range of applications. Laser range finders are used both by artillery officers to sight their guns and by surveyors. In outer space, where there is no atmosphere to absorb the light, the laser will supplement conventional radar and radio for space-vehicle navigation and communications.

Lasers can cut metal and other materials. But it is highly unlikely that a laser will ever replace an engine lathe or an oxyacetelene torch in most machining and metal-cutting operations. Lasers are being used in the precision machining of metals and in machining brittle materials such as diamonds.

A laser can weld metals as well as retinas. But here, too, its use is for precise work, as in making microelectronic circuits. Nevertheless, large lasers mounted atop high mountain peaks are being developed to provide a defense against intercontinental-ballistic-missile warheads.

To the scientist, the laser is already a valuable tool in absorption spectroscopy or the identification of compounds by the particular wavelengths of light that they absorb.

RADIANT ENERGY

How can a beam of light burn a hole in a steel plate? It can do so because light is a form of radiant energy, and a laser concentrates much radiant energy in a very tiny spot. Radiant energy exists in many forms besides visible light. It exists as radio waves, ultraviolet and infrared light, X rays, gamma rays, and even cosmic rays.

WAVELENGTH AND FREQUENCY

It is sometimes convenient to think of radiant energy as waves, that is, *electromagnetic waves*. Then the different forms of radiant energy can be classified by their *wavelengths* and arranged according to wavelength in a spectrum. We have all seen the waves made by a pebble thrown into a quiet pond. They are a series of alternating crests and troughs. The wavelength is defined as the distance between two adjacent crests or two adjacent troughs.

Now, when a wave goes from crest to trough and back to crest again, it is said to have gone through one cycle, or alternation. The number of cycles that a wave executes in one second is known as the *frequency* of the wave.

Light waves and all other electromagnetic waves travel at the same speed, which is 186,000 miles, or 300,000,000 meters, a second. All scientific measurements are made in metric system. In the metric system the basic unit of length is the meter—a little over three feet.

RADIO SPECTRUM

The alternating current supplied by the power company is an electromagnetic wave that executes 60 cycles a second; thus, in 1/60 of a second, or the time of one alternation, the wave will travel 300,000,000/60, or 5,000,000 meters—roughly the distance from New York to Los Angeles. The *electromagnetic spectrum* arranges the different kinds of electromagnetic energy according to decreasing wavelength.

Everyone is familiar with the red, orange, yellow, green, blue, and violet spectrum of the rainbow after a spring shower. The same separation of white light into its color components occurs when we pass light through a glass prism. A spectrum arranges the frequency components of white light according to decreasing wavelengths. Similar

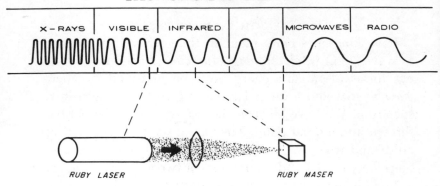

Electromagnetic spectrum from radio frequencies to X rays (Hughes)

spectra exist in the infrared and ultraviolet regions, but we can't see them. They can, however, be photographed by using special film. Radio waves also form part of the electromagnetic spectrum.

A radio broadcasting station with a frequency of 1,000 kilocycles per second (or cycles per second times 1,000) has a wave 300 meters long. A radar set used for navigation at sea has a wavelength of about 10 centimeters (one centimeter equals 1/100 meter), or approximately 4 inches.

VISIBLE SPECTRUM AND INFRARED

Radiant energy is invisible to the human eye only until we get to a wavelength of 0.00000075 meter, which we see as red light. Since the meter is an ungainly unit for measuring wavelengths of light, physicists use what is called the angstrom unit, abbreviated Å. One angstrom equals 1/10,000,000,000 meter. Therefore we can say the visible spectrum extends from 7,500 Å (deep red) to 4,000 Å, or blue. In between are regions of orange (about 6,000 Å), yellow (about 5,900 Å), and green (about 5,300 Å).

The visible spectrum is bounded by longer waves of

infrared that we sense as heat. For example, a jet engine exhaust has a wavelength of 40,000 Å, while the heat of the human body has a wavelength of about 99,000 Å.

FROM SUN TANS TO COSMIC RAYS

The short wavelength, or blue end of the spectrum, is bounded by the ultraviolet region. Sun-tanning ultraviolet rays have a wavelength of about 3,000 Å. Still shorter are X rays (150 to 10 Å) and gamma rays (1.4 to 0.1 Å). Gamma rays are associated with nuclear reactions, and account for some of the deadly effects of atomic and hydrogen bombs and of radioactive waste materials. At the high end of the spectrum are cosmic rays (0.01 to 0.001 Å), those weird visitors from outer space whose effects (they can cause biological mutations) are awesome indeed but about which very little is understood.

Scientists have known for a long time that the energy of radiation is proportional to its frequency. We cannot sense the presence of radio waves even though we stand close by the antenna of a powerful broadcasting station. Yet if we put a hand in front of a radar antenna, we may feel a slight sensation of warmth. The energy of ultraviolet waves will become painfully evident to some who sun bathe not wisely but too well. The penetrating power of X rays and gamma rays makes them useful for making shadowgraphs of the human skeleton and internal organs for medical diagnosis and for inspecting manufactured parts for hidden flaws. Indeed, hard, or short, X rays and gamma rays are used to destroy malignant tissue in the treatment of cancer and related diseases.

The energy of each wavelet of radiation is called a "quantum." It is measured by the frequency of the radiation multiplied by Planck's constant (this is equal to 6.625×10^{-27} erg seconds—26 zeros in front of the first

6). The intensity of a source of radiation depends upon the number of quanta emitted from it that pass a designated boundary at a given time.

FLUORESCENCE

The action of the laser is allied to another, more familiar, phenomenon, that of fluorescence. Fluorescence is said to occur when radiant energy hits the atoms or molecules of some particular material and in turn causes that substance to emit further radiant energy. Fluorescence has this important property: the emitted radiation is always at a lower frequency (longer wavelength) than the initial radiation.

Here's how scientists explain fluorescence: Every atom and molecule has certain energy states that it can occupy. When the atoms absorb energy, they move to higher energy states. Conversely, when they return to lower energy states, they give up energy, or emit radiation.

Imagine an atom to be a coil spring. When there is no compression on the spring, it is in its ground, or rest, state. When you compress the spring, you add potential energy to the system. When you release the spring, it bounces back and vibrates, giving up what is called its kinetic energy.

In the picture tube of your television set, electrons bombard a phosphor screen on the back of the faceplate. The kinetic energy, or energy of motion of the rapidly moving electrons, excites the atoms of the phosphor. As these atoms relax, the faceplate of the picture tube glows, and you see the television program because of fluorescence.

When a radiologist examines you with a fluoroscope, X rays penetrate your body and excite the atoms of a phosphor screen. As the atoms of the phosphor coating relax, the fluoroscope screen glows green, producing a shadowgraph of the part of the body being visualized.

In a neon sign, an alternating current creates an electromagnetic field that agitates the molecules of neon gas filling the tube. Because collisions of rapidly moving neon molecules raise these molecules to higher energy levels, they relax, emitting the orange-red glow characteristic of a neon sign.

Of course, the common fluorescent lamp works on the same principle of energy exchange. The inner walls of the lamp tube are coated with beryllium oxide. Inside the tube, there is an intense arc discharge between electrodes at either end of the lamp tube. This arc discharge is rich in ultraviolet light that energizes the phosphor molecules. As these molecules relax, the lamp emits a blue-white light similar to natural daylight.

We now have seen several examples of quantum energy exchanges, but no one ever burned a hole in a steel plate or illuminated the moon with a neon sign or with a fluorescent lamp. What, then, does the laser have that its less powerful cousins lack?

FREQUENCY COHERENCE

The answer is: the laser's coherence. In all the previous examples of the phenomenon of fluorescence, the emitted radiation had a broad spectrum. Because it was emitted in random fashion, some wavelets added together while others opposed each other.

Frequency coherence makes a big difference. It means that all the emitted energy has the same wavelength. When this happens, you can have a useful output indeed. Take the babble of voices at a cocktail party as an example of incoherent sound. The sound doesn't carry very far and it is not especially meaningful. But if you were to concentrate all that sound energy into the blast of a police whistle or siren, you could awaken half a city.

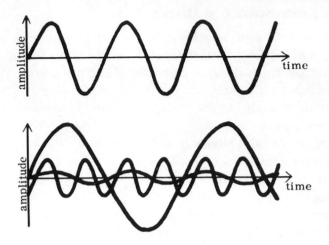

Frequency coherent radiation, top, and frequency incoherent radiation, bottom (Raytheon)

Engineers learned many years ago that they could communicate more efficiently and more meaningfully when they concentrated all the output of a radio transmitter at a single frequency. But frequency coherence has other advantages besides efficiency. A beam of coherent light can be modulated much as a radio signal can be. Modulation is a process by which intelligence such as music or speech is impressed upon a so-called carrier signal such as a radio wave.

An incoherent light beam can be modulated in only the most elementary manner—such as by switching it on and off, as with the visual blinker lights used to send Morse code between ships. But the frequency-coherent laser beam can be modulated by such complex signals as speech, music, or even a television picture.

Frequency-coherent light also lends itself to frequency multiplication, the technique whereby a closely controlled but relatively low radio frequency can be raised to a higher output frequency. The output of a ruby laser at

6,943 Å has been doubled to 3,472 Å. The input was deep red and the output blue-violet, almost ultraviolet. The reason the wavelengths of laser light are given so precisely is that the emission of laser light depends on the shifting of electrons between atomic orbits, and each wavelength is characteristic of one particular orbital shift, or so-called quantum jump.

Laser beams can also be mixed. For example, a ruby laser operates in two slightly different modes. These modes can be mixed in a microwave phototube. The frequency difference between the modes yields a microwave signal that can be handled by conventional radio or television techniques. This property has permitted some engineers to modulate laser beams with television pictures and to recover the television signal after transmission for several feet.

Scientists find the frequency coherence of the laser especially gratifying. Before the discovery of the laser, only signals in the lower, or radio, end of the spectrum could be produced coherently. Radio techniques were limited to producing signals whose wavelength was on the order of a millimeter or so.

If monochromatic (or single-frequency) signals were desired anywhere else in the spectrum, they had to be produced by placing an appropriate filter in front of an incoherent source. This method was unsatisfactory for two reasons: it was very inefficient, since the source had to produce many times the energy that could be usefully employed; and, second, since no filtered output is ever truly coherent, modulation, frequency multiplication, and mixing were always unsatisfactory. But now a whole new section of the spectrum, ranging from the "near" (to visible light, that is) infrared to near ultraviolet, is open to investigation, and there is evidence that the existing gaps at the high and low ends of this laser operating range can be filled by using related techniques.

Frequency coherence is only part of the picture. The output of a laser is also spatially coherent. This means that all wavelets start in step with each other. Spatial coherence also adds to the efficiency of a device. The difference

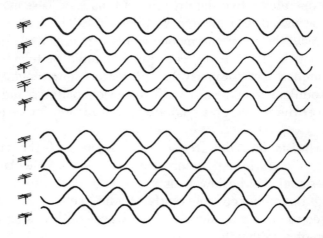

Spatially coherent radiation, top, and spatially incoherent radiation, bottom (Raytheon)

between spatial incoherence and spatial coherence is like the difference between a disorganized group of castaways of a raft each paddling in his own way and the smooth, efficient performance of a well-trained crew rowing an eight-oared racing shell.

RUBY LASERS

The ruby laser was the first device to generate coherent light successfully. The rubies used in lasers are synthetic gem stones. They are made by fusing aluminum and chromium oxides to produce large crystals. The amount of chromium in a synthetic ruby is small—about five hundredths of 1 percent. But it is that chromium upon which laser action depends.

The ruby crystal is cylindrical, about ¼ inch in diameter and 1½ to 2 inches long. It appears pink to the eye. That is because there are two absorption bands in a ruby—one at 5,600 Å and the other at 4,100 Å—which means that when you hold a ruby up to the light, yellow-green light and blue light are absorbed. This subtraction of yellow, green, and blue from white light (which is a mixture of all colors) gives the remaining light transmitted to the eye its distinctive pink hue. Actually, there is also some natural fluorescence in a ruby, but it is all but imperceptible to the eye.

A laser crystal must be polished to optical flatness on both ends. Both ends are also silvered, one with a heavy coat while the other, or output end, is lightly silvered with a coat that permits it to reflect only about 92 percent of light incident on it.

Exploded view of ruby laser showing ruby, mirrors, and helical flashtube (Hughes)

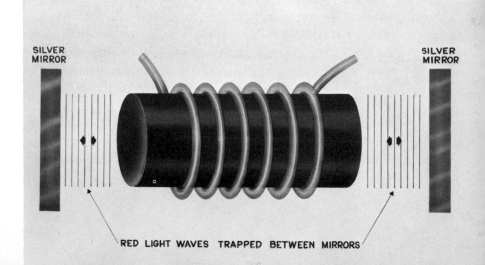

SILVER MIRROR   SILVER MIRROR

RED LIGHT WAVES TRAPPED BETWEEN MIRRORS

The ruby rod is now placed within a helical-shaped xenon flashtube, the kind of tube widely used in electronic flash attachments for cameras. The process of irradiating the ruby rod with a xenon flashtube is called optical pumping. The output of the flash lamp is rich in the yellow-green region.

The energy level of an atom (an ion is just an atom that has lost one or more electrons) depends upon the condition of its electrons. Now, an atom is like a miniature solar system. It has a positive nucleus at its center in place of the sun, and a specific number of planet-like electrons. These electrons revolve around the nucleus and spin on their own axes. Unlike the planets of the solar system, however, each electron can occupy not just one but several orbits. Moreover, the electrons can revolve around the nucleus with different azimuthal momenta (speed) and even change their direction of spin. Each change in orbit, momentum, or spin corresponds to a discrete energy level.

For example, when energy is imparted to an atom, an electron may move to an orbit more remote from the nucleus. The atom is said to absorb energy and to have been raised to a higher or more excited energy state or level. If the electron then returns to its original orbit, the atom gives up energy; it may now emit light of a certain precise wavelength. The atom is said to relax to a lower or less excited energy state or level. When light wavelets, or *photons*, at 5,600 Å from the flashtube irradiate the ruby rod, they raise the energy of some of the chromium ions dissolved in the ruby from ground state ① to various levels lying within the absorption band. Then the chromium ions immediately begin to drop from these higher energy levels. Some drop right back to the ground state—level ① —as they do in natural fluorescence. But others drop to

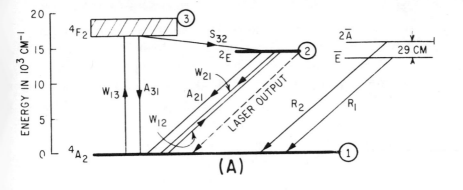

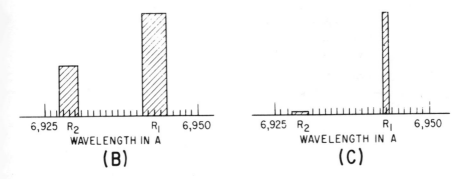

Energy level transitions in a ruby laser as described in text (A); low-level pumping (B) and high-level pumping (C) showing how latter mode concentrates energy at one wavelength (*Electronics*)

an intermediate or so-called *metastable state* ②. If left alone, the latter chromium ions would continue their drop to level ①, and the result would just be natural fluorescence. But these ions dally for a short but measurable time in level ②, and this is what makes laser action possible.

While the chromium ions are trying to get back to level ①, the flashtube keeps on irradiating more chromium ions.

In fact, the two-step movement from state ① to state ③ and down to state ② is much faster than the movement from state ② to state ①. Thus there develops a chromium-ion traffic jam at energy level ②.

STIMULATED EMISSION

As the pile-up of chromium ions in level ② continues, another situation develops: soon there are more chromium ions in level ② than in level ①. This is called *population inversion,* and is essential for laser action.

When you have inversion of the chromium ion population, the laser resembles a spring that is wound up and cocked. It needs a key to release it. This is what is meant by *stimulated emission* of radiation: the stimulus is the key that releases the cocked spring.

The key is a photon of light of exactly the wavelength to be emitted (6,943 Å). Emission begins when a random chromium ion spontaneously falls from level ② to level ① emitting a photon at 6,943 Å. The photon strikes neighboring metastable (level ②) ions, causing them to emit additional photons, and these in turn trigger other metastable ions.

As the photons travel along the rod, some emerge from the sides of the cylinder and are lost. Others hit the silvered ends of the cylinder and are reflected back into the rod. The reflections tend to favor those photons that are traveling parallel to the long axis of the cylinder. And so, there is now a stream of photons bouncing back and forth between the silvered ends of the cylinder. The pho-

Two following pages: How a ruby laser works. Pumping light irradiates ruby rod (A) raising some atoms to their metastable state (B). One atom spontaneously emits coherent radiation (C) triggering other nearby atoms (D). Photons emitted parallel to sides bounce back and forth between mirrors triggering other atoms (E) until light pulse (F) bursts from slightly transparent end *(Electronics)*

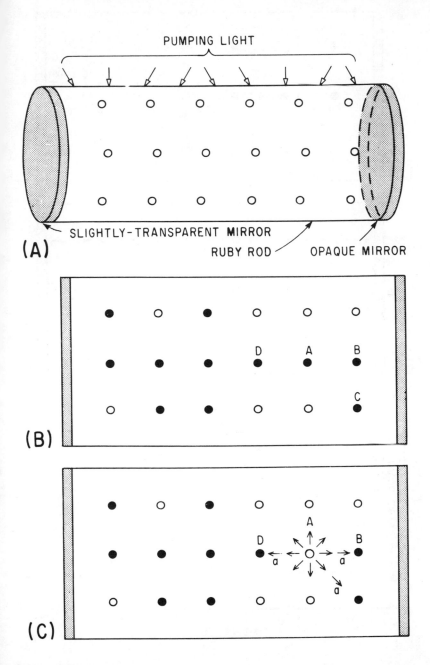

PUMPING LIGHT

SLIGHTLY-TRANSPARENT MIRROR
RUBY ROD   OPAQUE MIRROR

(A)

(B)

D A B
C

(C)

A
D   B
a   a
a

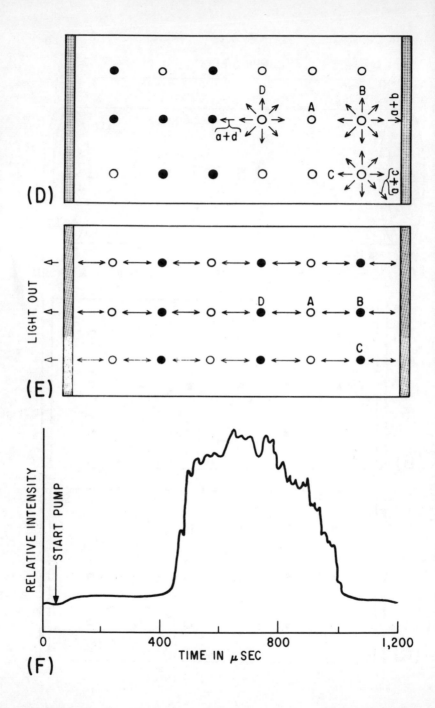

(D)

(E)

LIGHT OUT

(F)

RELATIVE INTENSITY

START PUMP

TIME IN μSEC

0   400   800   1,200

tons become more numerous, and consequently the light beam grows more intense as the photons already in the stream trigger still more metastable chromium ions into emitting their radiation.

Eventually the photon stream builds up sufficient intensity so that it bursts from the partially silvered end of the ruby as a single pulse of monochromatic (single color or frequency), spatially coherent light.

PARALLEL RAYS

The light beams coming out of the partially silvered end of the ruby rod are almost exactly parallel, and it is this factor that makes it possible for a laser beam to reach the moon. Conventional light sources such as an incandescent lamp are point sources: their light rays are emitted in a spherical pattern. Conventional rays can be made parallel by use of focusing mirrors and lenses, but such optical systems are far from efficient: the light beam diverges, and consequently loses its intensity at great distances. But since the beams coming from a laser are parallel to begin with, they remain essentially parallel even at exceedingly great distances.

LIQUID AND PLASTIC LASERS

The ruby laser was the first laser, but today it is only one member of the class of optically pumped lasers. Furthermore, there are many varieties of ruby lasers. The original ruby lasers worked at room temperature. Later devices have been designed to work at *cryogenic* temperatures, or temperatures close to absolute zero (—273 degrees centigrade). Cryogenic temperatures are usually achieved by immersing the laser in liquid nitrogen or liquid helium. Lasers cooled this way can put out a continuous beam of coherent light instead of a series of flashes.

Other optically pumped lasers include many different crystalline materials, most of which are *doped:* made impure by the infusion of small quantities of some other material—either a rare-earth element, such as europium or neodymium, or an actinide element—a class of heavy metals that includes uranium. Some optically pumped lasers have been made of doped glass (glass to which impurities have been added), of liquid or gas in a quartz cavity or of bundles of plastic fibers.

Gaseous Lasers

The gaseous laser represents a second general class of laser. The working medium is a mixture of helium and neon gas at very low pressure (0.1 millimeter of mercury

Helium-neon gas laser (Raytheon)

of neon and 1.0 millimeter of mercury of helium). The gas is contained in a cylindrical Pyrex tube about one meter long and 17 millimeters in diameter. At each end of the tube is a quartz plate ground optically flat and with a 13-layer dielectric (or electrically nonconductive) coating on its inner face: this coating produces the same effect as the lightly silvered end of the ruby rod. The spacing of the quartz-plate mirrors can be changed with precision for optimum internal reflection, thanks to an arrangement known as a *Fabry-Perot interferometer*. The laser beam is emitted from both ends of the apparatus.

ELECTRICAL PUMPING

The gas laser is not optically pumped, nor is it pulsed at the rate of three or four times a second as is the ruby laser. Instead it operates in a continuous-wave mode, its excitation supplied by a radio-frequency field—though in some gas lasers, direct current has been used to produce the required discharge. In a typical gas laser the source is a 50-watt transmitter operating on a carrier frequency of 29 megacycles per second. This frequency was selected simply because it lies within a band provided by the Federal Communications Commission for industrial, scientific, and medical use; another frequency would do equally well. The transmitter is coupled to the gas tube by three metal loops.

The radio-frequency generator produces an electrical discharge through the gas that raises the helium gas atoms to an excited state designated as the 2^3S state. This is a metastable state that the helium atoms retain for a finite period of time.

When the helium metastables collide with neon atoms in the ground state, the helium atoms transfer their energy to the neon atoms and drop immediately to the ground

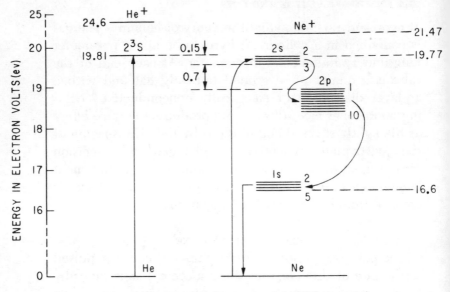

Energy levels in a helium-neon laser *(Electronics)*

state. Simultaneously, the neon atoms are raised to the so-called 2s state because the energy level of the 2s state in neon is nearly equal to the energy level of the 2^3S state in helium.

There are three excited states in neon that are involved in this reaction: the 2s, 2p, and 1s states. We are primarily interested in the transition between the 2s (higher) and 2p (lower) states. The 2s state is a metastable state. Actually, there are four substates in the 2s band and ten substates in the 2p band. Theoretically there are 30 possible transitions, or downward changes in energy level, that could occur, with each giving off radiation at its characteristic wavelength. Actually, only five of these transitions have as yet figured importantly in stimulated emissions; all correspond to wavelengths in the near-infrared region. The strongest of these emissions is one at 11,530 Å.

As in the case of the ruby laser, neon atoms tend to pile

up in the 2s state, and the threshold energy is the amount of input energy that makes the population of neon atoms in the 2s state equal to that in the 2p state. When some random neon atom spontaneously makes the transition from the 2s state to the 2p state, radiation at 11,530 Å stimulates coherent emission.

The photon at 11,530 Å stimulates nearby metastable neon atoms, and they, too, go down the chute and emit their photons at the same wavelength. Photons emitted perpendicular to the Fabry-Perot mirrors bounce back and forth between the mirrors until they acquire sufficient intensity to break out. Photons emitted in other directions are lost through the walls of the tube and do not participate in coherent emission.

When in operation, a gas laser is bathed in an orange-red glow, but this light has nothing to do with its laser action. Most of the coherent output of the gas laser is in the infrared region and is invisible to the eye. The visible glow results from spontaneous transitions of excited neon atoms that do not enter into the stimulated emission of radiation. In fact, the glow is identical to that of any neon sign.

Injection Lasers

The third basic type of laser is the injection laser. An injection laser consists of a semiconductor diode made of gallium arsenide or of gallium arsenide-phosphide.

A diode is an electronic part that has the property of conducting current easily in one direction but almost not at all in the opposite or reverse direction. The injection laser is a forward-biased semiconductor diode. It conducts current in its easy direction.

A semiconductor is a material that does not conduct electricity so well as something like copper does, but does so better than an insulator such as sulphur. The most common semiconductors are the metals silicon and germanium, but some compounds can also be used, and, for the injection laser, gallium arsenide has proved useful. Because gallium is a little better conductor than silicon, and arsenic a little poorer, when mixed together they give roughly the same effect as silicon.

Now, to make a diode out of a block of semiconductor material, it is necessary to dope it. This is done by allowing the two impurities—tellurium and zinc—to diffuse into the block at high temperature. Because the tellurium atom has one more valence (combining) electron than does arsenic, when tellurium atoms replace some of the arsenic atoms in the gallium-arsenic block, there are a few free electrons left over. Since the electron has a negative charge, tellurium-doped gallium arsenide is called N-type, or negative, gallium arsenide.

Because zinc, on the other hand, has one less valence electron than gallium, when some zinc atoms replace a few of the gallium atoms, there are several holes, or electron deficiencies, left over. Therefore, zinc-doped gallium arsenide is called P-type, or positive, gallium arsenide.

The boundary where the regions of N-type and P-type gallium arsenide meet is called the *semiconductor junction*. If you connect the positive terminal of a battery or electronic power supply to the P-type region of a semiconductor diode and connect the negative terminal to the N-type region, the diode will be biased in the forward direction, and current will flow easily across the semiconductor junction. If the power supply is connected with its negative terminal going to the P-region and its positive terminal going to the N-region, the diode will be biased in its reverse direction, and little, if any, current will flow across the semiconductor junction.

HOW DOES IT WORK?

Scientists are not yet sure just what energy transitions occur in the injection laser. But laser action seems to be most pronounced on the P-side of the junction. This might indicate that some energetic electrons making up the current flowing across the junction recombine with holes and give up energy in the recombination process.

The injection laser emits coherent light by passing extremely high current between the terminals of the semiconductor diode, so that light is emitted along the line that defines the semiconductor junction. The light comes out incoherently at first, but as the intensity of the current is increased, the emission becomes coherent. Of course, all

Semiconductor injection laser design as developed by IBM (*Electronics*)

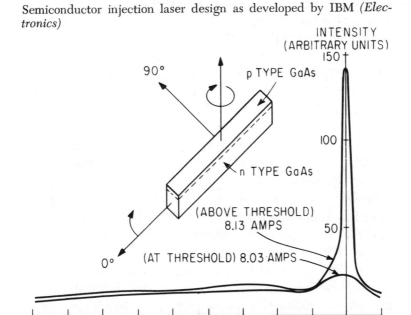

this electrical current passing through the relatively small diode makes the diode heat up rapidly. Since such extreme heating could destroy the semiconductor junction, before the diode is operated it is usually immersed in a cryostat, or double bottle, the inner bottle filled with liquid helium and the outer one with liquid nitrogen. Furthermore, the current is usually pulsed rather than passed continuously.

A typical injection laser is a rectangular parallelopiped (six-sided solid block whose opposite faces are parallel) about ten times as long as it is wide. Dimensions of a typical unit are 1/10 by 1/10 by 1¼ millimeters. The sides are finely polished and tend to reflect light back into the laser so that the emission of coherent light comes out in parallel rays from the square sides of the block. Silvering is not required because the block itself is metallic, and when its sides are polished they will reflect the light rays generated within the block.

Current is applied to opposite rectangular sides of the block. The current flow is perpendicular to the semiconductor junction, which is a narrow plane or region cutting the block along its long axis.

The reflection of waves at the polished sides of the diode tends to favor the waves coming out of the square ends parallel to the junction. Furthermore, since the recombination process takes place all along the semiconductor junction plane, coherent-light waves traveling along the junction stimulate radiation from other hole-electron pairs, and the wave grows in intensity before it bursts from the square sides of the laser.

A gallium-arsenide laser emits coherent light at 8,400 Å in the near-infrared region. This light is invisible to the human eye. Gallium arsenide-phosphide lasers have emitted coherent light at 7,000 Å, in the deep-red region. Furthermore, by varying the amount of phosphorus in the laser, the color can be changed throughout the near-infrared and deep-red regions of the spectrum. Several other intermetallic compounds involving indium and antimony as well as gallium, arsenic, and phosphorus show promise of producing laser action. A silicon-carbide diode was reported to have emitted blue-violet light, but proof of this accomplishment is as yet inconclusive.

The current passed through the particular laser we have described may vary from 10 to 25 amperes or more. At lower currents, the emission is incoherent and involves only a small part of the junction area. As current is increased, the area of incoherent sparkling or sporadic emission of light spreads out along the junction, and coherent emission can be noticed near the center of the junction.

Comparison

Thus there are three main types of lasers: optically pumped lasers, which may be crystalline, glass, liquid, gaseous, or plastic; radio-frequency or direct-current-pumped gas lasers; and semiconductor diode lasers pumped by injection of high current.

GASEOUS LASERS

The gas laser emits coherent light, usually in the infrared region. Gas lasers are used mostly in scientific investigations, such as spectroscopy, and for experiments in space and time, such as verification of some of the consequences of the theory of relativity. The gas laser is useful in these investigations because its output is the most nearly coherent of all lasers and because continuous output is conveniently available from gas lasers even at room temperature.

Because gaseous lasers operate in the continuous wave mode rather than through pulsation, they have proved

better than optically pumped lasers for many communications experiments, such as the transmission of speech
and music or television pictures.

Furthermore, since gas lasers produce the most nearly
coherent output of any laser—the only thing that can cause
a helium-neon gas laser to deviate from its 11,530 Å center
frequency is mechanical vibration of the apparatus—they
have been used for scientific studies, such as checking the
experimental evidence of Einstein's theory of relativity
and for constructing a precise gyroscope.

OPTICALLY PUMPED LASERS

Optically pumped lasers are used when high energy is
required, such as for burning metal, performing delicate
eye operations, precision welding or machining. The most
used optically pumped laser is still the ruby laser. It is
one of the few lasers that can give visible output. Nearly
all gas lasers, and most types of optically pumped lasers,
work in the infrared region. Most optically pumped lasers
emit pulses at a relatively low repetition rate. Continuous
output can be achieved only by putting the laser in a
cryostat, or double bottle of liquid helium and nitrogen.
Although the physical form of a ruby laser is simpler than
that of a gas laser, its excitation system is somewhat more
complex. The gas laser needs only a simple radio transmitter, while the ruby laser requires an electronic flashgun
and either a special xenon flashtube or a carefully designed
system of reflectors.

INJECTION LASERS

The injection laser is physically simpler than either the
ruby or gas laser. For excitation, it actually needs only a
rudimentary direct-current power supply, but it is usually
operated in a cryostat. Injection lasers can produce a
whole range of coherent output frequencies within the red

and infrared regions of the spectrum. They deliver continuous or nearly continuous output, and they, too, have been found useful in communications experiments in which speech, music, or even television pictures have been transmitted. Gallium-arsenide diodes operated at lower current and at room temperature are already being used in portable communications systems. Although the infrared output of these devices is not coherent, they have permitted communications over a range of thirty miles.

UNIVERSAL COHERENCE

Sciences have long dreamed of generating coherent emission at all frequencies of the electromagnetic spectrum. Quantum devices have made important contributions toward this end, but a great deal remains to be done. It has been suggested that variations of the word "maser" be coined for all the new devices, including the ones yet to come. There might be rasers (*r*adio-frequency), masers (*m*icrowave), irasers (*i*nfrared), lasers (*l*ight), uvasers (*uv*iolet), xasers (*X* ray), and gasers (*g*amma-ray). One prominent scientist jocularly suggested the name "daser," standing for "darkness amplification by stimulated emission of radiation."

All this points up the advantage of talking about quantum devices (and specifying whether they are oscillators, amplifiers, or harmonic generators) and designating the wavelength of interest rather than playing with acronyms. It does, nevertheless, seem to be a fact of life that the term "maser" will continue to be used both for amplifiers and for oscillators not only in the microwave region (roughly 1,000 megacycles per second) but perhaps for devices operating at even lower frequencies, when and if such devices are developed.

Likewise, it seems that the term "laser" will continue to

be used to refer both to amplifiers and to oscillators that operate in the near-infrared, visible, and near-ultraviolet portions of the spectrum. Neither extension of laser action into the far-infrared (near microwaves) nor into the far-ultraviolet (near X rays) will result in a change in terminology.

But possibly, when we can successfully generate coherent X rays and gamma rays, another term will be used, for already, as mentioned above, the word "gaser" is being bandied about.

MASERS

Masers are usually true amplifiers instead of the generators that lasers are. This means that they receive a weak signal and pass it on at a higher power level. Masers operate between 300 megacycles per second (100 centimeters or 1 meter wavelength) and 100,000 megacycles per second (3 millimeters).

We might remark parenthetically that there is other millimeter-wave research going on that does not involve masers. One special microwave tube, the Tornadotron, has been reported to have an output of 500,000 megacycles per second, or a wavelength of 0.6 millimeter.

A typical maser consists of a crystal containing chromium that is pumped by the output of a microwave tube operating at a frequency much higher than the one to be received. The microwave signal pumps the chromium ions to an elevated energy level that is metastable.

Incoming signals at a certain lower microwave frequency stimulate the chromium ions to fall from their elevated energy level to an intermediate level before the ground state. In so doing, they emit radiation at the frequency of the incoming signal and thus amplify it.

To avoid the introduction of noise or unwanted signals,

maser amplifiers are placed between the pole pieces of a powerful magnet, and are operated in a double bottle with liquid helium on the inside and liquid nitrogen on the outside.

About a dozen radio astronomical observatories throughout the world use maser amplifiers to pick up radio-frequency emissions from distant planets, stars, and nebulae. Several stations use maser amplifiers for tracking satellites and space probes. So do some of the stations that receive radio and television signals from orbiting communications satellites such as Telstar and Relay. It is possible that maser amplifiers are used in special military radar and communications applications, but if so, the Department of Defense isn't saying!

INFRARED LASERS (IRASERS)

Various kinds of lasers cover the near-infrared spectrum from nearly 13,000 Å right up to visible light. This leaves a gap in the spectrum from 3 millimeters wavelength to 0.013 millimeter. This gap includes the millimeter and submillimeter-wave regions of the radio spectrum and the far-infrared band that encompasses radiation from warm and lukewarm objects.

NEW COLORS IN LASERS

Progress has not been so good in the visible region. Only a few lasers produce visible light, and most of that, as we have noted, is deep red. There is, of course, the ruby laser. Red light has been produced by several other methods as well: by a laser consisting of a crystal of calcium fluoride with the rare-earth samarium dissolved in it; from europium chelate (rhymes with "tea late") embedded in a plastic tube (a chelate is a complex organic or hydrocarbon molecule containing a metal atom, in this case an atom of the rare-earth europium); with the gallium arsenide-phosphide laser; and with some helium-neon gas lasers.

There is a demand for lasers to produce other colors besides red. The Navy would like to have a blue-green laser because blue-green light is best for penetrating sea-water and because a blue-green laser could be used as part of an underwater television system to help navigators of nuclear submarines detect the presence of friendly or hostile submarines or other underwater objects.

So far, the only progress in that direction has been the development of "blue-violet lasers," produced by doubling the output frequency of a deep-red laser. (Doubling the output frequency is the same thing as dividing the wave-length by two.) Likewise, there are "green lasers," achieved by doubling the output frequency of lasers operating in the near-infrared region.

But when you double the output frequency of a laser, you lose 8/10 or more of its energy, and what's left will hardly perform the job the Navy has in mind. Therefore the search for different colored lasers continues, with scientists now studying not only rare-earth and actinide metals but even various organic compounds. They feel that, given the right conditions, any substance that will fluoresce can be made to lase. This leaves them with thousands of compounds to investigate.

ULTRAVIOLET LASERS (UVASERS)

So far the story of the ultraviolet laser is short and sweet. One optically pumped laser, using a glass rod in which a small quantity of the rare-earth gadolinium has been dissolved, lases at 3,125 Å in the near ultraviolet.

GAMMA-RAY LASERS (GASERS)

Nothing has been announced officially about X-ray lasers, but certain work is going on with gamma-ray lasers under Navy auspices, though the work has not progressed very far as yet. The Russians have also announced work in this field.

The approach is to use a gamma-ray-emitting isotope of ruthenium to raise a radioactive isotope of rhodium to a higher energy state that is metastable. After a half-life of some 40 days, the level of energy emitted by the ruthenium will drop to that of the metastable state of the rhodium isotope, and trigger emission at roughly 0.3 Å.

There are many problems in the way, however. First, one has to find a way to make a crystal containing the appropriate isotopes without changing their essential characteristics. Next comes the problem of containing the gamma rays (they will penetrate just about anything) so as to achieve spatial coherence. If achieved, a gamma-ray laser would be a death ray in every sense of the word. Gamma rays have several times the burning power of X rays, which are, of course, harmful when improperly applied.

THE FUTURE OF THE LASER

As we have seen, the laser has the advantage of providing a monochromatic or single-color light source. Furthermore, its beam is so collimated that all its energy can be focused on a very small spot. It is also highly directive, with little or no tendency for the beam to bend or spread out even over the astronomical distances of outer space. These properties have suggested a great many uses in national defense, industry, medicine, and science.

Lasers may be developed into devastating antipersonnel weapons for use on the battlefield. They may be sent into space on special platforms to fight intercontinental ballistic missiles or to destroy hostile space stations or satellites. The laser may also be used to modify chemical compounds or even to change the genetic characteristics of the protein molecules of living organisms.

Someday special fiber-optic light pipes or other optical wave guides, such as evacuated tubes with an internal mirror system, may carry laser signals much as coaxial cables now carry telephone conversations and network television programs between cities. A fiber-optic light pipe is a very fine glass, plastic, or arsenic-trisulfide rod polished on the outside; its walls reflect light back inside so that it can bend around corners and still carry a light beam.

One way to put a TV signal on a laser beam is first to impress the complete TV picture and sound (the video signal) on a microwave carrier. The microwave carrier is then used to excite a special crystal situated in a microwave cavity or special metal box. When the laser beam traverses the crystal, entering and leaving the cavity through small side windows, the beam is modulated or made to vary in accordance with the modulated microwave signal. At the receiver, the beam of a microwave traveling-wave amplifier phototube is similarly made to vary in accordance with the variations of the laser light striking the traveling wave tube's photocathode. We now have again the microwave carrier with the video signal riding on it. This signal is demodulated, using conventional electronic circuits to give the original TV picture and sound.

A wideband video channel can be divided into many subchannels, actually some 600, each of which can carry a telephone conversation. Electronic circuits called filters slice up the video channel into so-called voice channels. Each voice channel is about 0 to 2,000 cycles per second wide. Each incoming telephone signal is heterodyned, or moved up, in frequency to fit a specific voice channel at the transmitting end, then moved down in frequency and routed out on its proper telephone line at the receiving end.

A laser communications system would greatly expand the capabilities of our nationwide telecommunications network. Tiny lasers may also function as parts of the memory system of a computer. Such a computer would literally work with the speed of light.

Who knows? You may even one day have a laser ignition system in your automobile!

MILITARY USES

One of the first uses that occurs to most people is to build a big, superpower laser and use it to shoot down ballistic missile nose cones. This would, they reason, make our nation secure from the terrors of thermonuclear war.

But it isn't as easy as all that. Even the most powerful lasers can at present penetrate only ⅛-inch of high-carbon (easily burnable) steel. And the holes they make are mere pinpricks. Furthermore, burning requires that the laser be only a distance of a few feet from the steel. At longer ranges, the water vapor and dust in the atmosphere severely reduce the effective power of the light ray.

Nevertheless, the Air Force is hard at work trying to develop big lasers and figuring out how to deploy them effectively outside the earth's atmosphere: atop mountain peaks, aboard orbiting satellites, or even on antimissile missiles.

Meanwhile, the military and space agencies have other, more prosaic, but none the less vital uses for the laser. When the Apollo lunar capsule carries the first Americans to the vicinity of the moon, the two-man crew aboard the Lunar Excursion Module that will make the actual landing on the moon will probably use a laser altimeter to feel

their way onto the lunar surface. Before that, astronauts
in Project Gemini will use laser radar to practice rendezvous and docking of satellites in space. Already a large
laser at Wallops Island, Virginia, has tracked an orbiting
satellite 1,000 miles up. Incidentally, at that range the
laser beam was only 200 feet in diameter.

The Army has ordered several laser range finders for
use on the battlefield. They will be able to measure the
distance to targets far more accurately than their optical
or radar counterparts.

During World War II the Army made effective use of
sniperscopes and snooperscopes, infrared devices that located targets even at night. But for such devices to be
effective, the target had to be a good deal warmer than
the background. Now, with an infrared laser, it would be
possible to scan the target and get a picture regardless of
its temperature.

During World War II the Navy used infrared "Nancy"
equipment (usually Nerst tubes or hot filaments enclosed
by a black metal hood and placed behind a deep ruby
lens) for short-range communications between ships. But
the laser affords a much more efficient and less easily de-
tectable source of infrared.

The Armed Forces have a project under way to see just
how fast a computer can operate. Some people think that
the result will be a new high-speed giant brain for our
ballistic missile early-warning system. But a better guess
is that such a computer will be used to crack secret enemy
codes and ciphers. Anyway, one part of this project is a
laser computer, sponsored by the Air Force, in which light
pulses would do the counting instead of electrical signals.
Such a computer would be faster by several orders of
magnitude than any computer now available, since light
travels faster than electrical current, which is slowed

down by the action of reactive elements, such as capacitors and inductors in the circuit.

INDUSTRIAL APPLICATIONS

Industry is already using lasers to perform delicate machining and welding operations in the manufacture of microelectronic circuits.

A microelectronic circuit is fabricated on a thin wafer of silicon. Sometimes forty circuits are made at one time on a wafer only an inch in diameter. Each circuit can do the work of, say, a five-tube radio or perhaps a computer stage.

The circuits are made by allowing certain selected impurities to diffuse into the silicon wafer in prescribed patterns. These patterns are formed by first allowing a film of silicon dioxide (glass) to grow over the silicon wafer—usually by applying steam to the surface—then selectively etching away portions of the film.

Selective removal of the oxide is accomplished by first coating the oxide with so-called photoresist—a film that becomes tough and acid-resistant when exposed to light—then masking the wafer with a diffusion mask and exposing the unprotected photoresist to light. The wafer is next etched with strong acid, and its silicon-dioxide coat is eaten away except where it is protected by light-hardened photoresist.

Preparation of the diffusion mask is a critical operation, and laser machining of metallic foil is expected to allow making sharper and more precise pattern outlines. Possibly lasers may be used to remove the oxide itself, thus saving several steps in the process of manufacturing micro-circuits.

Laser light sources could be valuable in high-speed photography where chromatic aberration or the unequal bending of light of different wavelengths through the camera lens can cause a blurred image.

Since different components of the atmosphere absorb different wavelengths of light to a greater or lesser extent, a bank of lasers used at an airport as a transmissometer could disclose not only the visibility at the end of the runway—as the optical devices already in use do—but also the makeup of the atmosphere at any particular time. Such a laser device could also be useful in air-pollution studies. (Transmissometers are used even though the end of the runway may indeed be visible from the control tower; the view from the tower is not what an approaching pilot sees; besides, the instrument, unlike a human observer, remains on duty around the clock.)

In a chemical process, a laser might be created so that its beam is absorbed to a great extent by the desired product. The laser could be focused permanently through the output pipe, and automatic control equipment could be adjusted so that the product absorbs maximum light from the beam. This would assure that the product in the output pipe has precisely the desired chemical composition.

The ability of a laser beam to carry an almost infinite amount of information has set communications engineers to speculating about its possible use for trunkline or inter-city communications. Today, these are handled by coaxial cables or microwave links. One microwave link can carry four television programs simultaneously or replace any one of the television channels with up to 600 telephone conversations. But a laser beam could carry many times this amount of information.

Nevertheless, since dust and water vapor in the atmosphere severely reduce the effective power of a laser beam, a serious problem still remains before lasers can be used for practical communications. Of course, short-distance communications would indeed be possible, as would communications to and from communications satellites. In the latter case, the beam travels in the earth's atmosphere for only a relatively short distance, although the total trip might be 1,000 miles or even more.

One answer to abetting laser communications would be to use light pipes or evacuated tubes with mirrors arranged to conduct the beam around corners where necessary.

A laser telephone exchange has been contemplated. Here the light pulses would be conducted by fiber optic strands. These strands carry light around corners just as copper wires carry electrical current. Though a fiber-optic strand severely cuts down the power of the light being transmitted, in a telephone exchange the length of the interconnecting strands can be kept short by design. The big advantage of a laser telephone exchange would be that there would be no crossed wires or unwanted pickup between adjacent optical fibers so that you would not occasionally hear fragments of another conversation on your line.

MEDICAL USES

Lasers have been regarded as a major boon to medicine. Thousands of Americans suffer each year from a detached retina. In this condition the retina, the light or sensitive area at the rear of the eye, comes loose from the inner surface or choroid coating of the eyeball. The fluid, or humor, with which the eye is filled works in behind the retina and aggravates the condition. Initially, the condition causes distorted vision, but if the retina becomes completely loose from the optic nerve, blindness results. A laser beam can be focused through the lens of the eye so that it makes small scars around the periphery of the retina and thus welds it back into place.

A laser can also burn out small tumors in the eye. In fact, a laser beam can be made as narrow in diameter as the diameter of a single human cell. Some surgeons see the laser, therefore, as a device that can burn out tumors with minimum risk of damage to surrounding healthy tissue. Lasers have also been considered for suturing wounds through heat. The laser would cauterize the wound as it sutured it. It could also be used to disinfect small areas quickly. Dentists have experimented recently with laser drills; they are fast, sure, and painless.

It is conceivable that laser beams can be made even narrower in diameter than a single protein molecule. Such a laser beam might be used to alter the genetic properties of living organisms.

A team of medical scientists has reported that irradiation by a laser beam has altered the electrical conductivity of whole human blood. Just what this means or how it occurs has not yet been made apparent.

SCIENTIFIC APPLICATIONS

Perhaps some of the most far-reaching effects of the laser will be in the fields of pure and applied science. The laser may profoundly affect man's understanding of his natural environment.

Our most basic quantities of measurement are length, mass, and time. Two of these, length and time, are related by a constant, the velocity of light in a vacuum, and yet the value of this constant is only imperfectly known.

Our national standard of frequency is calibrated from the same astronomical observations that give us our measure of time, since the frequency of cycles per second that a wave executes is intimately related to time.

When dealing with radiation in the visible region, scientists measure wavelength instead of frequency. But if the standard radio frequencies could be doubled, redoubled, and then redoubled again as many times as necessary to reach the visible-light region, then length and time would be one and the same thing irrespective of our uncertainty as to the exact speed of light in a vacuum.

Another basic scientific problem is the question of whether ether exists or not. You recall that we explained electromagnetic waves by comparing them to waves in a pond. Many scientists have found it equally hard to conceive of waves without postulating some substance or medium in which the waves could move or propagate.

Accordingly, they postulated ether—a colorless, odorless substance filling all space—in which electromagnetic waves could propagate just as waves propagate in a pond. For years now, scientists have been trying to relegate ether to the same never-never land as phlogiston and other weird substances once postulated by alchemists to explain physical phenomena they could not understand.

The first experiment to disprove the existence of ether was the Michaelson-Morley experiment: If the earth is rotating in a stationary sea of ether, the ether will drift by the earth in a direction counter to the earth's rotation. Now, suppose two light beams are transmitted at right angles to each other in such a way that the ether drift will add to the speed of one beam while the other beam will travel perpendicular to the ether drift and therefore be unaffected by it. Then any difference in velocity caused by ether drift could be detected by measuring the difference in frequency of the two beams. To make the measurement more precise, the apparatus emitting the light beam is next turned around so that the ether drift will oppose the speed of the beam instead of adding to it; the frequency difference (if any) can again be measured. If the sum of the two frequency differences were significant, an ether drift could be said to exist. This experiment has been carried out with the use of gas lasers, but no significant frequency difference has been noticed that could substantiate the existence of an ether.

In the realm of applied science, the laser shows greatest promise in spectroscopy. We have referred at many times to absorption of infrared, light, and ultraviolet frequencies by certain substances. The exact frequencies absorbed depend upon the chemical composition of the substance and the structure of its molecules. The totality of frequencies absorbed or the absorption spectrum of a substance is as individual as your fingerprints. Therefore spectroscopy is a basic tool for physicists and chemists studying the properties of matter. But better discrimination in spectroscopy is needed, and to get it, scientists must know the exact frequencies with which a substance is irradiated. As the number of laser materials increases, and consequently the number of available coherent light frequencies increases, spectroscopists can look forward to more efficient tools that will enable them to gain greater and greater insight into the basic makeup of matter.

CONCLUSION

In this chapter we have explained the continuum of the electromagnetic spectrum in terms of both frequency and wavelength. We have come to grips with some of the basic concepts of quantum mechanics and have seen how they explain the action of the three basic types of lasers: optically pumped, gaseous electrically pumped, and injection. We have discussed the phenomenon of fluorescence and have seen how laser action is related to fluorescence but differs from it because of (a) its frequency coherence or monochromaticity and (b) its spatial coherence, or the fact that all wavelets keep in step.

(Incidentally, this last gem of knowledge now makes you smarter than a certain covey of investors with more spare cash than technical knowledge. They lost several kilobucks supporting a glib physicist with a lab full of bottles of fluorescent material that he passed off as lasers completely covering the visible spectrum! Of course, they weren't lasers at all.)

Finally, we have looked at the whole electromagnetic spectrum in terms of how coherent radiation is or might be produced by quantum devices, and have placed a special emphasis on a possible gamma-ray laser. And we have seen the impact of lasers on national defense, industry, medicine, and science.

Now we shall look backward and see how the laser actually came into being.

II

WHAT LED TO THE INVENTION

LINKING LIGHT AND ELECTRICITY

The beginnings of the story of the laser go back to man's first attempts to find a uniform explanation for the two phenomena of light and electricity.

Around the middle of the nineteenth century, scientists were really beginning to understand electricity. Back in 1819, Hans Christian Oersted, professor of physics at the University of Copenhagen, had verified the relationship between magnetism and electricity by observing the behavior of a magnetic-compass needle when placed close to a current-carrying wire.

Michael Faraday, formerly an English bookbinder's apprentice, had invented the dynamo, or electric generator, in 1831.

MAXWELL AND HIS EQUATIONS

A studious young Scotsman, James Clerk Maxwell, was one of Faraday's greatest admirers. It is said that Maxwell studied the theories and experiments of Faraday with something like religious reverence. Maxwell, who eventually set up the famous Cavendish laboratory at Cambridge, was on the faculty of King's College, London, when in 1863 he wrote with elegant mathematical simplicity the equations for the propagation of electromagnetic waves.

60

Reasoning that electromagnetic energy moved through space with a wavelike motion, he calculated the velocity at which these waves traveled. He found it to be the same velocity as that of light and therefore deduced that light must be a form of electromagnetic energy.

Unfortunately, in Maxwell's day there was no way of generating what we would call radio-frequency waves. And Maxwell died in 1879, before his theories could ever be tested.

HERTZ: FATHER OF RADIO

But they were indeed put to the test a few years later. Heinrich Rudolph Hertz, professor of physics at the University of Bonn, succeeded in generating radio waves in 1887 and in detecting them over distances. He made a heavy spark jump from a Leyden jar, a type of electrical capacitor used by the pioneers in electrical science, and observed that a smaller spark jumped across a small gap in a loop of wire some fifteen feet away.

From 1887 to 1891, Hertz experimented with radio waves. His transmitter consisted of an induction coil, like the one used in a car's ignition system, connected to two

Hertz's first radio transmitter and receiver *(Electronics)*

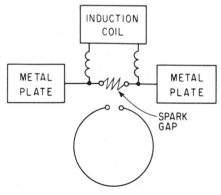

brass spheres. The spheres were each attached by rods to two large metal conductors about three meters apart. Between the spheres was a gap across which sparks jumped when the induction coil was energized. Each time a spark jumped across the gap, an electric charge oscillated rapidly between the metal plates, perhaps ten to one hundred million times a second.

For a receiver, Hertz used a loop or rectangle of thick copper wire cut to provide a small gap at one point. On each side of the gap he attached a highly polished brass knob about a half-inch in diameter. The width of the gap could be adjusted as desired by bending the loop of copper wire.

The loop was held horizontally so that the brass knobs of the transmitter faced the knobs of the receiver. When the transmitter was energized and the receiver properly adjusted, a series of small sparks bridged the air gap of the receiver even when the two instruments were several feet apart. This distance was too far for the phenomenon to be explained by simple induction. And Hertz found that he could pass this radiation through a glass window or a brick wall as well as through free space.

Then Hertz made a large prism out of pitch or asphalt. He found that his electromagnetic waves were bent or refracted by the asphalt prism in the same general way that light waves are refracted by a glass prism.

When Hertz put a large vertical sheet of metal in front of his transmitter, he found that not only were the electromagnetic waves totally reflected but also that a so-called standing-wave pattern was set up between the transmitter and the receiver. (A standing-wave pattern consists of alternating contours of maximum and minimum energy, contours that can be detected if the receiver is moved back and forth in the region between the transmitter and the reflecting metal sheet. The contours of maximum intensity are separated by one-half the wavelength of the frequency being transmitted. This standing-wave pattern resembles Newton's rings or the interference patterns observed when monochromatic or single-color light is partially reflected between two nearly parallel glass plates.)

Hertz worked between frequencies of 10 and 100 megacycles per second. In an effort to bridge the gap between electromagnetic waves and light, he made his apparatus smaller and smaller. It is said that his experiments took him even into the millimeter-wave region.

He invented many kinds of antennas, the Hertz, or two-element dipole, horns and paraboloidal dishes. He even used circular copper pipe or wave guide to carry his radiation. Incidentally, many of Hertz's devices were "reinvented" when radar became important during World War II.

But Hertz never bridged the gap between radio waves and light, although his experiments provided abundant evidence that, as Maxwell had predicted, the two phenomena were one and the same thing since both behaved in much the same way, and the higher the frequency of the radio waves, the more they acted like light.

Developing Quantum Theory

Bridging the spectrum gap would have to be left to other men, other times, and other techniques. The first clue to the laser came, strangely enough, from the field of thermodynamics, the study of heat and its effects.

THE BLACK-BODY ENIGMA

One classical puzzle that interested thermodynamicists in the late nineteenth century was the behavior of the black-body radiator. Think of an airtight box or hollow sphere, made perhaps of iron. Its inside is lined with a thick layer of felt, and over the felt is a uniform layer of lampblack or soot to provide a smooth flat surface. Such an enclosure absorbs all the visible energy directed into it and reflects none at all, since of all the absorbers of light, the black body is the most perfect.

Now, imagine that the black body is completely sealed up, except for a small hole, and that heat and light, supplied by a glowing platinum filament focused by a system of lenses, are introduced into the enclosure.

The energy bounces around from inner wall to inner wall and is ultimately absorbed by the lampblack surface. The final effect of heat and light energy directed into a black-body enclosure is to raise the temperature of the black body. A hot black body gives off the maximum amount of radiant energy with the widest possible range of infrared and visible frequencies.

Even back in the 1890's it was possible to measure the amount and frequency of radiant energy, with a fair degree of accuracy, by the use of an instrument known as a bolometer. The bolometer was shielded with an infrared or visible-light filter that permitted only radiation of the frequency being measured to pass through. With a bolometer and a suitable set of filters, a physicist could measure the amount of radiation from a body at every frequency.

In the black-body studies of the late nineteenth century, a bolometer and filter were inserted into the hole of the black body after the black body had been heated to some predetermined temperature. Using different filters, the physicist took enough readings to plot a smooth curve of energy against wavelength. Then the black body was heated further to a second predetermined temperature,

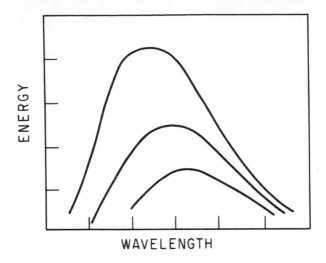

WAVELENGTH

Black-body radiation curves showing variation in energy with frequency *(Electronics)*

and enough readings were taken to plot a second curve of
radiated energy against wavelength.

These experiments were performed over a whole range
of temperatures, and the results presented an enigma to
physicists of the day. As was expected, the area under the
curve, or the total radiant energy emitted by the hot black
body, increased with every increase in temperature of the
black body. But something unexpected happened, too. The
distribution of radiant energy according to wavelength
also changed with temperature!

At low temperatures, both the radiant energy clustered
around a few closely spaced wavelengths in the far-infrared region of the electromagnetic spectrum and the peak
value of the radiant energy were high. At moderate temperatures, the wavelengths of radiant energy spread out
more widely through the near-infrared region, but the
peak value was somewhat lower in intensity. At high
temperatures, the wavelengths of radiant energy spread

out broadly throughout the infrared and visual-energy regions, and the peak value of radiant energy was still lower.

Physicists explored many theories and hypotheses, trying to find one that would explain the behavior of the black body, but without success. The problem simply would not yield to classical thermodynamic theory.

PLANCK AND HIS CONSTANT

Finally, in 1900, Max Planck, a German professor of thermodynamics, took an unorthodox approach to the black-body problem.

If classical theory will not provide an equation to describe the behavior of the black body, he reasoned, why not create an equation that will do so, and forget about classical theory?

Generally speaking, such a "curve-fitting" approach is not only unorthodox but unwise. In sophomore engineering courses it is called "fudging" the data. It is frowned upon in scientific circles for the simple reason that a fitted curve usually meshes with only one set of data and is proved invalid when another scientist finds newer data.

But although physicists of the day paid little attention to Planck's theories, he continued with his work. Planck reasoned that each lampblack molecule could be looked upon as a little generator of high-frequency energy that vibrates under the influence of the heat energy supplied.

So far Planck's theory coincided with classical theory. But Planck broke with his contemporaries in that he postulated that these microscopic generators could receive and transmit energy only in discrete amounts. Suppose, for example, that the smallest amount of energy that an oscillator (or generator of radiant energy) can generate is the quantity E. Then we can have $2E$, $3E$, $10E$, $92E$ but never

3.1416E or 6.5E or 13.9E. In other words, we must have an integral or whole-number multiple of the smallest amount of energy permitted.

Planck found that the energy of an oscillator (in ergs) was equal to the frequency of radiation in cycles per second times a constant. This constant, naturally enough, is called Planck's constant. It is equal to 6.6258×10^{-27} erg-second.

Planck's theory is also known as the quantum theory. It conceives of energy traveling in packets rather than in continuous waves. It provides the theoretical basis for the operation of the laser and the maser. All the work of Einstein and our modern physicists begins with the once-tenuous "ad hoc" hypothesis of Max Planck.

PHOTOELECTRICITY

In 1889, Hertz made a series of observations that set the stage for the second act of the drama of quantum electronics. He noticed that when a sheet of glass was placed between the spark gap of his transmitter and the receiver, it was more difficult to excite sparks at the receiver. He reasoned that when the glass plate was not present, ultraviolet light from the transmitter spark discharge fell on the burnished brass knobs of the receiver, which was only a few feet away. This ultraviolet light ionized the air around the knobs, thereby making the air an electricity conductor and the spark easier to excite. The glass plate intercepted the ultraviolet light and so made the spark more difficult to excite. From these observations, Hertz was able to deduce the nature of the phenomenon of photoelectricity.

EINSTEIN'S PHOTON THEORY

Some years later, Albert Einstein, then a clerk in the Swiss patent office, studied another manifestation of photoelectricity. When light strikes the surface of a zinc plate, each electron that is released has a certain kinetic energy, as shown by the velocity with which the electron leaves the zinc plate. In the days B.Q.T. (Before Quantum Theory) it might have seemed reasonable to expect that by using a more intense light, one might produce more energetic, or faster-moving, electrons. This is not true, however. A more intense light produces more electrons, but they all have the same old velocity. To get more energetic, that is, faster, electrons, one has to irradiate the zinc plate with a light source having a shorter wavelength, such as a light source rich in ultraviolet—like an arc discharge or one of Professor Hertz's sparks.

Einstein tried to arrive at a mathematical formula describing the photoelectric emission of an electron from the zinc plate. He was struck with the similarity between his electrical problem and the thermodynamic one for which Max Planck had just postulated a solution. And the analogy held. Einstein found he could equate the quantum energy of the incident light ray (the product of its frequency and Planck's constant) to the sum of the kinetic energy of the liberated electron plus another quantity that proved to be a property of the photosensitive material under study. Einstein called this quantity the "work function" of the material.

Einstein published his photon theory in 1905, the same year in which he published his special theory of relativity —thereby forever confusing the two subjects in the minds of physics students. Einstein had brought the quantum theory from the domain of thermodynamics into the wider realms of light and electricity.

CHASING RAINBOWS

Now the spectroscopists assumed a major role in the

development of quantum electronics. And they have played a major role ever since.

The major object of spectroscopic study in the early part of this century was the hydrogen atom, a logical choice because it consists only of a single electron rotating around a single proton. The spectroscopists found hydrogen had three spectra.

When a substance is excited by being heated or by being placed in an electric arc, it gives off a characteristic bright-line, or emission, spectrum. Its white-hot glow has several frequency components whose intensities are higher than the rest. All these intense-frequency components taken collectively make up the emission spectrum of the substance.

Hydrogen has one emission spectrum in the visual region. This spectrum was discovered by Johann Balmer, a Swiss physicist in the late nineteenth century. Within the hydrogen spectrum the four principal intense frequencies, or so-called spectral lines, are 6,563 Å, 4,861 Å, 4,340 Å, and 4,102 Å. Balmer found that these lines formed a distinct mathematical progression.

Later, another spectrum for hydrogen was found in the ultraviolet region by Theodore Lyman, an American physicist, while a third was found in the infrared region by Friedrich Paschen, a German spectroscopist.

BOHR: A PEEK INTO THE ATOM

Now, in the light of the quantum theory, each of these lines corresponded to a certain quantum of energy. But what did they all mean? In 1913, Niels Bohr, the great Danish physicist, answered this question by postulating that a hydrogen atom had a number of definite rings or shells in which its electron could rotate around the nucleus. The rings farther out correspond to higher energy states, and the rings closer to the proton correspond to lower energy states.

When the electron drops from an outer ring to an inner ring, it emits photons corresponding to a characteristic bright spectrum line. All the permissible shifts of orbit taken collectively make up the bright-line, or emission, spectrum, which can then be used to identify the substance. Similarly, when the electron moves from an inner ring to an outer ring, it absorbs a certain quantum of energy.

Bohr's work gave a good picture of what went on inside the atom.

Good, but not good enough! Though the Bohr atom was adequate for hydrogen, it failed to explain many effects that continued to trouble physicists—effects observed in heavier atoms having many more electrons than hydrogen and in molecules or collections of similar or dissimilar atoms.

QUANTUM MECHANICS

There are bands instead of definite spectral lines in these heavier atoms, and the Bohr model was just too simple to explain these effects. The big advance came with the discovery of quantum mechanics—a discovery made quite independently by two investigators in the same year, 1925.

Werner Heisenberg, a German physicist, arrived at his answers by working with the results of spectroscopic investigations and formulating them into a then new mathematical device called the matrix. His results were first called matrix mechanics.

An Austrian physicist, Erwin Schrödinger, came upon essentially the same result by another route. His work depended upon previous studies by a Frenchman, Louis de

Broglie. De Broglie answered once for all the conundrum that still confuses some junior high school science students: Is an electron a particle moving at high speed or is it a wave? De Broglie showed that any fast-moving particle can be considered as a wave and that it is amenable to the same mathematical treatment as a wave is.

Thus Schrödinger applied a probabilistic treatment to the classical wave equation and came out with an elegant mathematical formulation known, naturally, as Schrödinger's wave equation. His work became known as wave mechanics.

Because of the very complex mathematics associated with the work of both Schrödinger and Heisenberg, people did not immediately recognize that matrix mechanics and wave mechanics were two sides of the same coin. However, their connection did become apparent, and since the late 1920's we have spoken about quantum mechanics, the science that gave man his first real understanding of what goes on inside the atom and that today permits physicists to predict what substances will lase, at what frequencies and with what energy levels of input energy. However, quantum mechanics is an exceedingly complex subject, and these predictions are often necessarily rough approximations. There is still room for an infinite amount of painstaking experimental study.

The Prophecy Stage of Lasers and Masers

The laser and maser were both predicted long before the science of quantum mechanics was born.

EINSTEIN: STIMULATED EMISSION

In 1917, Albert Einstein found that in order to explain thermal equilibrium in a gas that was absorbing and emitting radiation (for example, in a glowing tube of gas in

which the amount of heat let in equals the amount of heat
let out, and there is, therefore, no change in temperature),
he had to postulate a certain induced emission of radiation.

He showed that there were three processes involved;
namely, absorption, spontaneous emission (fluorescence),
and stimulated emission—or lasing, as it was later called.
But because under normal conditions the first two processes are dominant, the last was not considered an important effect.

HEITLER: INDUCED EMISSION

Stimulated emission was described under the name "induced emission" by Walter Heitler, an Irish physicist edu-
cated in Germany and teaching in Zurich, Switzerland.
Heitler's book, *The Quantum Theory of Radiation,* appeared in 1954.

WEBER: THE MASER PRINCIPLE

Maser amplification was described in principle only—
without a working device—at an Electron Tube Research
Conference in Ottawa, Canada, in 1952, by Joseph Weber,
a young professor of electrical engineering at the University of Maryland and a consultant to the United States
Naval Ordnance Laboratory. Weber, an Annapolis gradu-
ate and former naval officer, was then a doctoral candidate at Catholic University in Washington, D.C. He is
a specialist in quantum electrodynamics and microwave
spectroscopy.

FABRIKANT: RUSSIA'S CONTENDER

And, as usual, the Russians will probably one day claim
to have invented both the laser and the maser.

A patent now bearing the date of June 18, 1951, was
awarded to V. A. Fabrikant of the Moscow Power Insti-

tute. Actually, Fabrikant's patent wasn't published until 1959. At first the Soviet Patent Office turned him down. And he didn't build a maser or a laser, either. In the Soviet Union you can patent the formulation of physical laws or descriptions of physical properties of phenomena as well as new inventions.

Fabrikant's patent reads "Method of amplifying electromagnetic radiation (ultraviolet, visible, infrared, and radio wave bands) distinguished by the fact that the amplified radiation is pased through a medium which, by means of auxiliary radiation, or by other means, generates excess concentration, in comparison with the equilibrium concentration, of atoms, other particles, or systems at upper energy levels corresponding to excited states."

This covers just about everything connected with laser or maser action. However, Fabrikant's work seems to have been concerned solely with what we would now call a gascous laser, and there is no evidence that he actually obtained laser action in practice. Later, important work in gas lasers was done at Lebedev Institute of Physics in Moscow by N. G. Basov and A. M. Prokhorov.

TRIAL OF THE MASER

All of which brings us to Charles H. Townes, true father of the maser, the precursor of the laser. Interested in almost everything, Townes is a Renaissance man cut from the cloth of a Da Vinci and transplanted into our century. In a world of narrow, workaday specialists, he is almost as interesting personally as are the devices he fathered.

CHARLES H. TOWNES: INVENTOR OF THE MASER

Townes, although famous primarily as a physicist and teacher, is also a skindiver, mountain climber, world traveler, a breeder of exotic orchids, former vice president of a major national defense advisory corporation, and master of at least four foreign languages.

It is hard to resist the temptation to characterize Charles Townes as looking like a church deacon. And indeed he was once a deacon of Manhattan's Riverside Church near Columbia University. Moreover, he has been a choir singer and a Boy Scout leader.

Townes describes the reactions that one gets from witnessing a new scientific discovery as a tremendous emotional experience akin to a religious experience, a revelation.

For Charles Townes, the trail to the first maser began in 1931 in his home town of Greenville, North Carolina, when as a sixteen-year-old boy he entered Furman University. Although he soon discovered his dedication to physics, Townes also studied deeply in the humanities: Greek, Latin, Anglo-Saxon, French, and German. He won a B.A. degree in modern languages after three years at Furman. After his fourth year, he received a B.S. in physics.

Next, Townes went to Duke University on a scholarship. At twenty-one he finished work on his master's degree, while studying courses in French, Russian, and Italian.

Then Townes went westward from his native North Carolina to one of the Meccas of science students, California Institute of Technology in Pasadena. He received his Ph.D. in 1939, just in time to meet an appointment with fate—World War II.

THROUGH RADAR TO THE MASER

Townes accepted an appointment at Bell Telephone Laboratories. At first, he started out on the Laboratories' training course for young scientists with a slow intro-

Charles H. Townes *(right)*, inventor of the maser, and Ali Javan *(left)*, inventor of the gas laser, prepare to check on Einstein's theory of relativity *(Electronics)*

duction to the various departments of the laboratories.

But the war was already under way in Europe, and soon Townes was assigned to work with Dean Wooldridge, one day to join with another radar engineer, Simon Ramo, to form the famous Ramo-Wooldridge Corporation. In those days, Wooldridge was designing radar bombing systems.

Although Townes found theoretical physics more to his liking than radar gadgeteering, it was this wartime introduction to microwave electronics that put him on the trail of the maser.

During World War II, the running duel between radarmen and operators employing jamming equipment against radar forced radar designers ever upward in frequency. Operational radar sets for airborne use eventually hit 10,000 megacycles per second in frequency, or three centimeters in wavelength.

Then the Air Force asked Bell to work on a radar for 24,000 megacycles per second. Such a radar, the Air Force reasoned, would exploit an almost virgin frequency range as far as radar went, and would result in more precise bombing equipment, too.

Townes, however, remembered that electromagnetic radiation in this 1¼-centimeter wavelength region was strongly absorbed by the invisible water vapor always present in the air. But the Air Force wanted to give it a try. So Townes built and tested the equipment, and, as he had predicted, it didn't work very well.

But the Air Force got its money back manyfold from this failure because the work interested Townes in microwave spectroscopy, and out of his interest were born the maser and the laser and a generation of weapons with a potentiality greater than any radar bombing system could ever be.

Townes learned that 1¼-centimeter waves were absorbed by ammonia as well as by water vapor. He measured how much energy absorption occurred under different experimental conditions and studied the reasons why this absorption happened.

In 1947, Townes accepted a suggestion from Isidor I. Rabi, distinguished Columbia University physicist, that he leave Bell Laboratories and join the faculty of Columbia. Townes soon became a leading authority on microwave spectroscopy or the use of microwaves to discover the secrets of matter. In 1950, two years after joining the faculty, Townes became a full professor of physics.

CONCEPTION OF THE MASER

Early in 1950, the Office of Naval Research sponsored a committee of scientists and engineers to study the problems of producing millimeter and submillimeter waves. Townes worked nearly two seasons on the committee and found himself deeply dissatisfied with its progress and the outlook for the future.

Then, in the spring of 1951, came the revelation that led directly to the maser. Townes was in Washington, D.C., to attend the next meeting of the committee. One morning he arose at dawn, dressed quietly so as not to disturb his brother-in-law, Arthur L. Schawlow of Bell Labs, with whom he was sharing a hotel room. Here's how he describes what went on in the gray Washington dawn: "I found myself sitting on a bench in Franklin Park admiring the azaleas, then at the height of their bloom, but also wondering whether there was a real key to the production of very short electromagnetic waves."

Until then, very short waves had been produced by making the cavities or so-called resonators in which the waves built up strength smaller and smaller. But there is a limit to how small man can make things. Then what about the atoms and molecules of matter itself? Why not use them for resonators?

Physicists had historically steered clear of this course because the thermodynamics specialists had argued convincingly that molecules could not radiate more energy than the old black-body or ideal thermal radiator. But recent experiments with molecular beams tended to show that the thermodynamicists' argument wasn't always valid.

Townes continues: "In a few minutes I had calculated, on the usual back of an envelope, the critical condition for oscillation in terms of the number of excited molecules

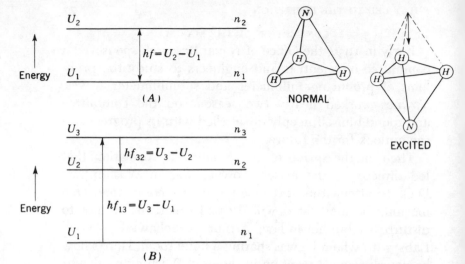

Energy levels in the two-level ammonia-beam maser, left, and configurations of the ammonia molecule, right *(Electronics)*

which must be supplied and the maximum losses allowable in the cavity."

He did not discuss his ideas with his fellow committee members but waited until he got back to his own laboratory at Columbia to start work on his new concept of amplification.

Here were some of the ideas that set Townes off on the trail of the maser. If you could see a molecule of ammonia gas, it would look like a tetrahedron, or four-sided pyramid. At each corner of the pyramid is an atom. There is a single atom of nitrogen at the apex of the pyramid, and there are three atoms of hydrogen at the three corners of its base.

When ammonia gas is irradiated with microwave energy at a frequency of 24,000 megacycles per second, the pyramid of atoms literally turns itself inside out. The nitrogen atom tunnels through the base formed by the three hydrogen atoms to make a sort of mirror image of the basic ammonia molecule. When this happens, the molecule is said to be in an excited state.

Usually, when a bag of ammonia gas is irradiated, as many excited molecules spontaneously slip from their excited state back to the ground state as are raised from the ground state to the excited state. This is called equilibrium, and when substances are in equilibrium the old argument of the thermodynamacists is valid indeed. No such substance can radiate any more energy than any ordinary hot body.

But, Townes argued, suppose the excited molecules could be pulled off by themselves so that a region existed where excited molecules outnumbered the molecules in the ground state. Could not the excited molecules then be made to radiate enough energy to make up a molecular microwave generator? Townes thought they could, and set about proving it.

THE AMMONIA-BEAM MASER

He gathered around him a group of researchers, including H. J. Zeiger, a postdoctoral fellow, and James P. Gordon, then a doctoral candidate. Their plan was to use a strong electrostatic field to form excited ammonia molecules into a beam and to focus the beam through a small hole in a box or cavity that was tuned to exactly 24,000 megacycles per second.

By concentrating the excited ammonia molecules in the box, Townes hoped to achieve population inversion, or a surplus of excited molecules. After achieving this condition any excited molecule slipping back to the ground state could trigger the rest of the molecules into relaxing and make the box emit coherent radiation at 24,000 megacycles per second. In those days, this action had been predicted under the name of "negative absorption." Then by continuing to squirt his beam of excited molecules into the small hole in the cavity, coherent oscillation could be sustained almost indefinitely.

Townes says he felt Gordon in particular had undertaken a somewhat risky venture on which to stake his doctoral research. "I'm not sure it will work," he admitted, "but there are other things we can do with it if it doesn't."

For two years Townes and his colleagues built gadgets, tested, tore them down, and then rebuilt. About this time two friends called at the laboratory and urged Townes to give up this silly molecular-amplifier business and stop wasting government money. Townes was far from happy at this point, for he had indeed spent $50,000 under a joint services grant administered by the Signal Corps, and the molecular amplifier seemed no closer to reality than ever.

Then one day very late in 1953, Jim Gordon rushed into a spectroscopy seminar that Townes was attending with the long-awaited news: the maser was oscillating!

The story goes that Townes, Gordon, and the other students (Zeiger had by this time left Columbia to go to Lincoln Laboratory, a huge government research complex operated by Massachusetts Institute of Technology) went straight to a local basement restaurant to celebrate. They searched without success for a short Latin or Greek name for the new device.

But it wasn't until later another evening that with the help of the students they coined the acronym maser: *m*icrowave *a*mplification by *s*timulated *e*mission of *r*adiation. Townes concedes that maser can also have another meaning in this day of big government-sponsored research: *m*eans of *a*cquiring *s*upport for *e*xpensive *r*esearch.

After discovering the maser, which Townes himself

modestly credits "to the triumph and glory" of James Gordon, he wasn't really sure what it was good for.

It wasn't an amplifier at all but an oscillator. And it stubbornly insisted on oscillating precisely at only one frequency; it could not be tuned, not even over a narrow range.

As it turned out, this frequency stability was the crowning glory of the ammonia-beam maser, and not a drawback at all. Furthermore, this maser made a splendid clock. Until the discovery of the maser, the very best clocks in the world could be expected to accumulate errors at the rate of about one second every ten years. But the molecular-beam "clock" accumulated errors at the rate of only one second every 10,000 years. The ammonia-beam maser thus became an accurate standard of frequency (though there are today even better molecular clocks using cesium or rubidium vapors).

BLOEMBERGEN: TUNABLE MASERS

Once the maser became a reality, Professor Townes took a sabbatical leave from Columbia and settled in Paris. There, in 1955, he hit upon an idea for a tunable maser. He would work with paramagnetic substances. Paramagnetic materials are metals or metallic salts that can be magnetized—not so strongly as a truly magnetic material such as iron—but of course more so than a nonmagnetic material such as copper.

In a magnetic field paramagnetic materials possess energy levels that are determined by the orientation of electron spins. (The electron, while rotating around its nucleus as the earth rotates around the sun, spins on its own axis just as the earth does.) The electron spins can be lined up in either of two ways—*with* the magnetic field, corresponding to the ground state; or *against* the field, corresponding to the excited state.

The quantum frequency depends upon the value of magnetic-field strength. Thus, if the quantum differences in paramagnetic material could be exploited to obtain maser action, such a maser could be tuned by varying the magnetic-field strength. It would not be restricted to a unique frequency as was the ammonia-beam maser. Townes tried out his theory with the metal germanium, but this time his efforts were not blessed with success.

Meanwhile, Nicolaas Bloembergen, a professor of physics at Harvard University, suggested another approach to achieving maser action with paramagnetic materials. He felt that a maser using three, not two, energy levels would make a more convenient and usable amplifier.

Bloembergen, then thirty-six years old, was born in Dordrecht, Netherlands. He received his doctorate in physics from the University of Utrecht in 1943, while the Germans were occupying Holland. He then escaped from his occupied homeland with the help of the Dutch underground, and eventually went to Harvard. At Harvard he began the studies of nuclear magnetic resonance that were to contribute to his theory of the three-level solid-state maser.

Bloembergen returned briefly to the Netherlands after the war and continued his research at the University of Leyden, where he received a doctor of philosophy degree in 1948. He returned to Harvard, and in 1956, told the world how to build a workable maser amplifier.

Briefly, Bloembergen's ideas were as follows: In a substance whose atoms have one electron free or missing from the so-called crystal-lattice structure, electrons lined up *with* a magnetic field can be considered to be in the ground, or unexcited, state. Electrons lined up *against* the

Nicolaas Bloembergen, father of the solid-state maser *(Electronics)*

field can be considered to be in an excited state. Now this is just where we left Charles Townes in Paris working with his arsenic-doped or N-type germanium device.

But, Bloembergen continued, when a substance has more than one electron missing, there is more than one possible excited energy state. In fact, there is one excited state for every missing, or free, electron. Under normal conditions, there would be a statistical distribution of electron spins between the ground state and all the excited states. The majority of the electrons would be in the ground state, of course; and the higher the energy state, the fewer the electrons there would be in it.

However, in the three-level maser a strong microwave signal or pump could be used to raise electrons from the ground state to the uppermost of two excited states. Population inversion would occur when the uppermost excited state possessed more electrons than the first excited or intermediate state. After this has happened, the quantum-mechanical spring could be considered to be cocked.

If another microwave signal of lower frequency, corresponding to the energy difference between the two excited states, were allowed to irradiate the maser crystal, the electrons would fall from the uppermost energy level to the intermediate one, and in so doing give up microwave energy that would amplify the incoming microwave signal that triggered their slide down the quantum hill. This arrangement would make a true maser amplifier; moreover, it would be one that could amplify continuously because the microwave pump was independent of the incoming signal and could replenish the topmost energy level even while the electrons were sliding down to the intermediate level to amplify the incoming signal.

SOLID-STATE MASER

By now the scientific world was eagerly following every development in quantum electronics, and soon a dozen laboratories were trying to build a three-level maser according to Professor Bloembergen's theory. A Bell Telephone Laboratories team of H. E. D. Scovil, G. Feher, and H. Seidel produced the first solid-state maser, although it was, in fact, an oscillator and not really an amplifier. It generated microwave signals rather than intensifying signals received from another source, as did Townes original ammonia-beam device.

At MIT's Lincoln Laboratory, Alan L. McWhorter and

James W. Meyer, inventor of the solid-state maser amplifier, and his creation (*Electronics*)

James W. Meyer were first to measure certain of the new amplifier's characteristics, and went on to build an improved device.

James Meyer of Lincoln Laboratory is a husky Missourian who did a stint in the prewar regular Navy as a radio technician. Before delving into physics, he had risen from Apprentice Seaman to Lieutenant, j.g. His maser, the first true amplifier, uses the paramagnetic salt, potassium cobaltocyanide with five-tenths of one percent chromium added.

The chromium is the important constituent. It has three

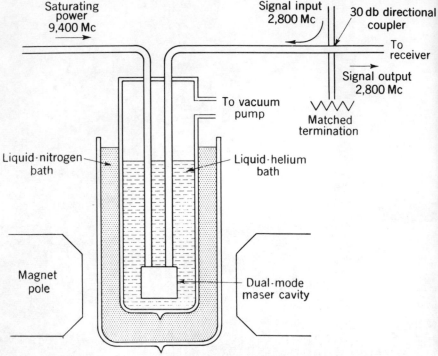

Solid-state maser amplifier *(Electronics)*

free electrons. This means there are three excited-energy states available, though only two are actually used.

The maser is operated in a double thermos bottle, or so-called dewar flask. The inner bottle contains liquid helium, the outer bottle liquid nitrogen. In this solid-state maser, the chrome salt crystal is kept at a temperature only 1¼ centigrade degrees above absolute zero. This greatly reduces the amount of pump power needed.

A powerful electromagnet provides the magnetic field across the crystal, and the pumping energy is supplied by a klystron, or radar tube, operating continuously at 9,400 megacycles per second. The signals to be amplified find their own way in and out at a frequency of 2,800 megacycles per second. Of course, by varying the magnetic field, a different combination of pump and signal frequencies could be obtained, but the microwave hardware associated with the maser would have to be changed, too.

Lincoln Laboratory soon attached one of these masers to the receiver of the high-powered radar installed on Millstone Hill near Boston. This radar was for a long time our keenest eye on space: able to keep our Air Force and space agency up-to-date on where our artificial earth satellites and those of the USSR were and what they were doing. This radar also served as a "test bed" for trying out designs for even more advanced space-tracking radars now installed on our missile test ranges and elsewhere in the world.

Bloembergen himself built a solid-state maser and attached it to Harvard University's radio telescope, where it is still listening in on microwave energy emissions from distant galaxies and nebulae.

MASERS AND THE SPACE AGE

Masers are highly sensitive, low-noise radio amplifiers with two major applications: in radio (passive) and radar (active) astronomy and in space radio communications.

As far back as 1931, Karl Jansky, then at Bell Laboratories, found that certain heavenly bodies gave off not only visible light but also radio signals. Astronomers then began studying these radio signals to gather additional information about the heavens.

For example, the hydrogen gas that exists in the space between the stars gives off a very distinctive radio signal; its radio emissions have been used in acquiring information about distant galaxies, groups of stars similar to our own Milky Way.

Radio astronomy has added to man's knowledge of the sun and of planets such as Venus and Jupiter. A strong radio source was discovered in the constellation Cygnus, the swan, where man had previously not been able to find a visible star. With the radio signals as a guide, astronomers at Mount Palomar observatory near Los Angeles aimed their powerful 200-inch reflecting telescope at the spot and received faint visual indications of a star.

Therefore radio astronomy has provided a way of studying galaxies so distant that they are beyond the range of optical telescopes. As a result, there has been a race among astronomers to build bigger and bigger radio antennas, usually paraboloids, or huge metal saucers. But there is a limit to how big a dish can be built, supported, and steered accurately—a proposed 600-foot dish designed for the Navy came to grief at least partly on this account.

But a maser amplifier can provide a radio telescope using a 50-foot dish with all the sensitivity of a radio telescope using a 500-foot dish. Since Bloembergen first hooked his solid-state maser to Harvard's 60-foot radio telescope, the maser has been adding new dimensions to the work of radio astronomers.

Meyer's maser, attached to the receiver of MIT's Millstone Hill radar, has spawned a whole progeny of powerful space-tracking radars. Not only have these radars tracked missiles and satellites; they have also mapped the surface of the moon, Mars, and Venus, and have probed the blistering face of the sun itself. The Air Force's giant 1,000-foot radar telescope now being carved out of a mountainside near Arecibo, Puerto Rico, will use a maser preamplifier for its receiver.

H-BOMB-PROOF COMMUNICATIONS

Since maser amplifiers make radio amplifiers from 100

Fifty-foot radio telescope atop Naval Research Laboratory uses a maser amplifier (USN)

to 1,000 times better than can other preamplifiers, they are invaluable in space radio. The Air Force's Project Westford uses them at both ends of an intercontinental space radio link between Westford, Massachusetts, and Camp Parks, California.

The purpose of this project is to dispel one of the nightmares of modern war: the possible silencing of long-range radio communications by an atomic bomb explosion in the ionosphere. Conventional long-range radio depends upon bouncing signals off the ionosphere, the layers of electrically conducting gas that exist at heights from 60 to 400 miles above the earth. But we know that an atomic bomb exploded in this region will stop long-range radio communications for anywhere from 15 to 45 minutes.

Many of our military leaders feel that the first thing that would happen in a sneak nuclear attack against us would be the detonation of at least one 50-megaton hydrogen bomb in the ionosphere above our country; we could then be hit with missiles or even with manned bombers while our Armed Forces were unable to communicate.

Thus Project Westford's problem: Can we communicate without the ionosphere? Answer: We can and do. Using maser-equipped receivers, the Air Force first sent information from coast-to-coast at the rate of 50,000 bits per second (a bit is a basic measure of quantity of information: it takes only about four bits to send a letter of the alphabet) by bouncing a microwave beam off the moon. Then they bounced their beam off the Echo satellite, a 100-foot balloon of silver plastic. Today they are bouncing signals off our orbiting belt of tiny copper needles.

TALKING TO SATELLITES

Naturally, when communications satellites came on the

scene, maser preamplifiers were there in force. The first was attached to a giant 400-square-foot horn antenna built by Bell Laboratories at Holmdel, New Jersey. It was used originally to bounce signals off the Echo satellite. Then a second giant horn antenna was built near Andover, Maine, and both were used to receive television pictures from the Telstar satellites.

Today similar stations equipped with masers are operating in England, France, Germany, Italy, Brazil, and Japan. They receive microwave signals from Telstar and Relay satellites and soon will be working with more advanced communications satellites such as Syncom.

The kinds of information carried over satellite communications links now include not only television pictures and sound but also multiple telephone conversations, transmission of photographs in both black-and-white, and color, Teletypesetter signals that compose newspaper pages ready for printing, computer data, and even human heartbeats as recorded by an electrocardiograph.

BIRTH OF THE LASER

Thus far what is past is prologue as far as the laser is concerned. By 1957, Charles H. Townes was again impatient with progress in the field of masers. Although masers had by then provided man with more accurate standards of frequency and time than had ever been dreamed of, and with amplifiers of greater sensitivity and lower noise than one might have dared ask for, still the masers had failed to penetrate into the spectroscopic no-man's-land between microwaves and the infrared.

What's more, an assault on this front seemed as unlikely as ever. The molecular beam oscillators required a tuned cavity to provide the boost or feedback necessary to sustain oscillation. And engineers again came up against the problem: How small can you build a box? In this respect the maser still hadn't solved anything.

Furthermore, the solid-state maser required a microwave pumping frequency higher than that of the incoming signal to be amplified. So engineers went back to diddling with klystrons, just where they left off after World War II. The maser had resulted in some extremely precise and stable oscillators and some perfectly fine amplifiers, but no new frequency ranges had been opened up. The no-man's-land was still terra incognita to scientists.

TOWNES AND SCHAWLOW: PREDICTIONS

Now Townes looked at the obverse of his problem. If one could not successfully penetrate the unknown frequency region by moving upward from the microwave region, why not then move downward from visible light?

The optical spectra of a host of materials were well known to physicists. Techniques for working in this region were also well known. Calculations showed Townes that masers could be made to operate in the optical region using known spectroscopic energy transitions and reflecting cavities as resonators.

Townes was now joined in his calculations by his brother-in-law, Arthur L. Schawlow, a research physicist at Bell Labs. Although born in Mount Vernon, New York, just outside New York City, Schawlow had won his B.A., M.A., and Ph.D. degrees, all in physics, from the University of Toronto in Canada. Before going to Bell Labs, Schawlow had been a postdoctoral fellow at Columbia. Previously, he had collaborated with Townes on a textbook on microwave spectroscopy.

Now Schawlow and Townes addressed themselves to setting down the conditions for making an optical maser (later to be called the laser). They considered using two

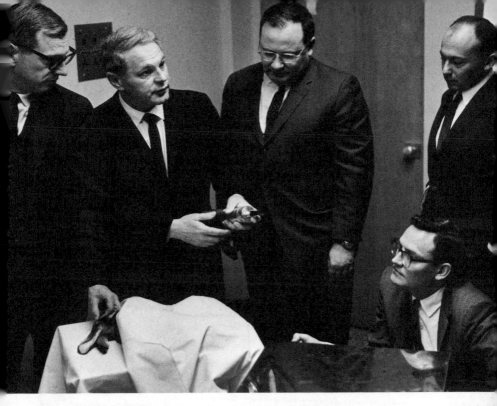

Palo Alto Medical Research Foundation team conducting ophthalmic laser experiment on rabbit. Team members are Dr. H. C. Zweng, Dr. Milton Flocks, and Professor Arthur L. Schawlow of Stanford, and Norman Peppers and Norman Silbertrust of Optics Technology. The first laser operation for the detached retina of a human patient was performed by the two Stanford surgeons on Stanford's own Director of Electronics and Radio Sciences Division *(Electronics)*

parallel flat mirrors between which there would be a collection of atoms most of which were in excited-energy states.

As in the microwave maser, a single quantum of energy —but this time light energy—emitted spontaneously from one atom can trigger or stimulate emission from others. If this stimulated emission is directed perpendicular to the two parallel mirrors, the light is reflected back and forth

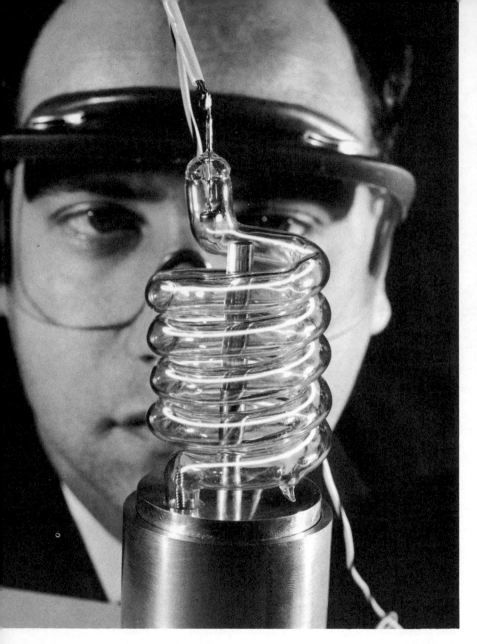

Theodore H. Maiman, inventor of the ruby laser, studies its main parts (Hughes)

between the mirrors. And if the total amount of light emitted from the atoms is greater than the losses incurred by reflection from the mirrors, the light wave gains in intensity during the process. Light photons not emitted in the direction perpendicular to the mirrors spew off into space and do not enter into the action.

Ultimately, the wave saps the energy of all the excited atoms in the space and it cannot grow further. At this point, steady oscillation is attained.

Such an oscillator, Townes and Schawlow declared, would be coherent in space, with all light quanta exactly in step, and it would be pure in frequency, although singing at a frequency near one billion megacycles per second!

When Schawlow and Townes published their hypothesis in 1958, they set off a new wave of activity in scientific laboratories from coast to coast, as scientists and engineers scrambled to build a working model of the device hypothesized by Schawlow and Townes.

MAIMAN: INVENTOR OF THE RUBY LASER

In fact it was in Southern California, a continent away from New York's Columbia University, that the breakthrough finally occurred. That was in July, 1960, at Hughes Research Laboratories in Malibu, when a ruby crystal irradiated by a xenon flash lamp produced a needle-sharp beam of coherent, monochromatic deep-red light.

Inventor of the laser was Theodore H. Maiman, youthful head of the Hughes quantum electronics section. Ted Maiman took his B.S. in engineering physics at the University of Colorado and received an M.S. in electrical engineering and a Ph.D. in physics, both from Stanford University. His Ph.D. was only five years old at the time he invented the laser.

At Stanford, Maiman had done his doctoral research

in microwave spectroscopy. He had also worked as an electronic engineer doing diverse gadgeteering with radio and television transmitters, control systems, and electronic test instruments. And he had been a research scientist at Lockheed Aircraft for a short while, where he studied communications problems associated with guided missiles.

In his five years at Hughes prior to the inventing of the laser, Maiman had worked on refinements of the maser. He developed the first maser cooled with liquid nitrogen and, later, one cooled with dry ice.

After inventing the laser, Maiman left Hughes, first to become vice president and director of the applied-physics laboratory for Quantatron, Inc., and later to become president of the Korad Corporation, a subsidiary of Union Carbide.

Maiman's laser was an unpretentious-looking device. The so-called head, or business, end of the laser was an aluminum cylinder only two inches long and one inch in diameter.

In announcing his discovery to the press, Maiman called it an atomic radio-light brighter than the center of the sun. He pointed out that his achievement marked the culmination of a major industrial research effort, some of which was privately supported and some supported by government funds. Hughes's effort, he declared, was done with the company's own money.

He said the laser could be used as a light radar to direct light waves to targets in outer space and get back a picture of a clarity never before attainable.

Maiman felt that the needle-sharp light beam could assure for television and voice communications a private line secure from static and resistant even to deliberate jamming.

He suggested a wide range of uses for the laser in biology, medicine, and industry, pointing out that the laser beam, focused to a needlepoint, could sterilize surfaces and even vaporize individual parts of bacteria, small plants, and particles. Surface areas, he predicted, could be modified by chemical and metallurgical changes induced by the laser beam's light and heat.

But despite major improvements made in the ruby laser by a research group at Bell Laboratories, the device remained unsatisfactory for many purposes. As we have noted it operated at a rather high power level, and then only in pulses. Furthermore, its output was not entirely monochromatic or single frequency.

JAVAN: THE GAS LASER

In 1961, a Bell Laboratories group consisting of Ali Javan, William R. Bennett, and D. R. Herriott invented the gaseous laser. Javan, who later moved on to MIT, used a small radio transmitter—the kind used in amateur radio—to excite an electrical discharge in a quartz tube filled with a mixture of helium and neon gases. The discharge excited the helium atoms which then transferred their energy to neon atoms making the number of neon atoms in an upper excited state larger than the number of neon atoms in intermediate energy states. This action fulfilled the conditions for laser action.

The gas laser was especially attractive in that it oscillated continuously, not in pulses as the ruby laser did. Furthermore, it could be precisely controlled to give the highest degree of frequency purity of any laser. Also, its efficiency was close to the best that could theoretically be expected from any laser. And it represented the first beachhead in Townes's no-man's-land of spectroscopy. The laser beam, however, was not in the visible range, but, instead, in the invisible infrared region.

REDIKER, NATHAN, HALL: THE INJECTION LASER

Then, in the fall of 1962, a new type of laser appeared. This was the so-called injection laser. It was announced simultaneously by three groups: one at MIT's Lincoln Laboratory led by Robert H. Rediker; a second at International Business Machines' Yorktown Heights, New York, research center under Marshall I. Nathan; and a third group led by Robert N. Hall at the General Electric Research Laboratory, Schenectady, New York. Shortly thereafter, research groups at General Telephone and Electronics research center in Bayside, New York, at Texas Instruments Incorporated in Dallas, Texas, and at Bell Labs announced similar work.

The injection laser, as we know, is actually a forward-biased gallium arsenide or gallium arsenide-phosphide diode.

Physicists had long been interested in the way a gallium-phosphide diode sparkled with tiny scintillations of bright red light when a current was passed through it.

Then it was noted that a gallium-arsenide diode gave off infrared radiation when current went through it in a forward direction. When the current was modulated or varied in response to some sort of intelligence, the infrared radiation emitted by the diode also varied in its amplitude.

Bob Rediker's group at Lincoln Lab sent a television picture on a beam of infrared light emitted by a gallium-arsenide diode. At first they were able to transmit intelligence only a few feet, but then, using an improved apparatus fitted with lenses and paraboloidal reflectors, Rediker succeeded in sending messages thirty miles between two Massachusetts hilltops.

In fact, Texas Instruments began manufacturing gallium-arsenide infrared diodes for use in short-distance communications systems. So far, however, all these emis-

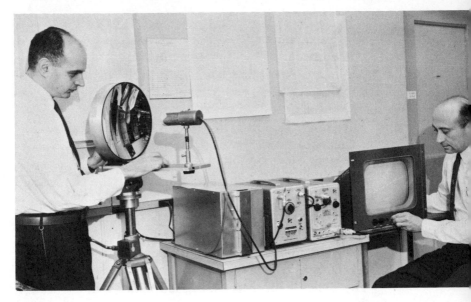

Inventors of the injection laser: *Above*, Robert H. Rediker of MIT *(standing)*. *Below*, *left*, Marshall I. Nathan *(seated)*, and, *right*, Robert N. Hall *(Electronics*, IBM, GE)

sions were incoherent. No laser action had been observed.

Then it occurred to the research groups at Lincoln Lab, IBM, and General Electric respectively to increase the magnitude of the current passing through the junction and see what happened.

Since this was hard to do without burning out the diode, the scientists found that they had to operate their diodes at liquid nitrogen temperatures and that they had to pulse the current rather than send it through the diode continuously.

When they reached a current density of some ten thousand amperes per square centimeter, the incoherent infrared radiation of the gallium-arsenide diode became coherent, and true laser action was attained.

The General Electric group soon found that by using a gallium arsenide-phosphide diode, coherent emission of deep red light could be obtained and that varying the amount of phosphorus seemed to affect the wavelength of emitted radiation.

Thus the injection laser offered unique properties compared with the ruby and gaseous lasers. It could not oscillate continuously, but it could be pulsed at a far more rapid rate than the gas laser. Furthermore, the intensity of its emission was easily controlled by varying the amplitude of the current through it.

RECENT DEVELOPMENTS

All three types of lasers have undergone intensive development since their invention. The ruby laser has spawned a whole host of optically pumped lasers using many different materials. First, there were various different solid-state crystals. Then came gas sealed in a tube, and later various organic liquids, lasers made of glass with rare-earth metal dissolved in it, and finally even plastic lasers. Some optically pumped lasers no longer need operate in pulses, since under certain conditions they can be made to operate continuously.

Nor is the output of optically pumped lasers any longer confined to deep red. Some optically pumped lasers put out infrared radiation; one emits ultraviolet. So far, visible colors other than red can be achieved only by frequency multiplication, that is, by passing a near-infrared beam through a special crystal. But this process is highly inefficient.

Gaseous lasers are still gaseous, and most still operate in the infrared region. However, it has been found that a direct-current electrical discharge, as well as a radio-freqency source, can operate a gaseous laser. Various combinations of gases besides helium and neon have produced gaseous lasers that emit dozens of different wavelengths throughout the near-infrared region. Modulating the radio-frequency excitation of a gas laser has proved to be a simple method for impressing intelligence on the beam.

And so we have seen how the history of the laser is the history of man's quest to link the two phenomena of light and electricity. The effort spans a whole century from James Clerk Maxwell's superb intellectual achievement in writing his electromagnetic wave equations in 1863 to the injection lasers of Rediker, Nathan, and Hall announced at the end of 1962. Although the laser grew out of the work of almost all the great men of modern physics —Hertz, Planck, Einstein, Schrödinger, and Heisenberg —its proximate origins go back only a dozen years to the spring morning in 1951 when Charles H. Townes sat on a park bench in Washington, D.C., gazing at the azaleas.

III

LASERS IN WAR AND PEACE

The laser has, it is said, blazed a path across the scientific horizon, leaving in its wake a trail of broken toy balloons and pierced razor blades. The sarcasm results from the fact that in one of the most familiar demonstrations of its strength, the beam from a ruby laser has been used to pierce a razor blade and the toy balloon behind it. The lasers for these trials are usually six-inch-long, ⅜-inch-diameter ruby rods with a suitcase-sized power supply.

In other demonstrations, lasers have vaporized small carbon blocks and heated balls of steel wool to incandescence.

MILITARY APPLICATIONS: LIMITATIONS AND POSSIBILITIES

From demonstrations like these, optimists have supposed that all we need do is build bigger and more powerful lasers and—*voilà*—we shall have a true disintegrator death ray right out of science fiction. We could then deploy batteries of these fearsome weapons and vaporize enemy tanks, airplanes, soldiers, even guided-missile nose cones.

And we could forget about all the expensive, old-fashioned gadgets like rifles, machine guns, cannons—even radar, missiles, and nuclear bombs.

But it is one thing to burn a pinhole in a razor blade and quite another to pierce a tank. And there is a big difference between popping a toy balloon a few feet away and vaporizing the warhead of a T-2 missile re-entering the earth's atmosphere at 18,000 miles per hour.

The laser, then, like most everything else, has its limitations. To begin with, the ruby laser, the only type seriously considered today for weapons use, is highly inefficient. Only about 1 percent of all the energy pumped into the laser comes out as coherent light.

The other 99 percent has to go somewhere, and so it appears as heat. Thus engineers have the tremendous problem of cooling a large laser head. To do so, they, as we have noted, have to use cryostats or special Thermos bottles filled with liquid helium, liquid nitrogen, or both. Such complex cooling systems are more than a little out of place on the battlefield!

Meanwhile, however, considerable progress has been made in developing more efficient optical pumps. Such a pump would not generate its light energy promiscuously at all wavelengths from near infrared all the way to ultraviolet. Rather it would concentrate it at the specific bluegreen wavelength that the ruby laser absorbs best. Some scientists have speculated about using one laser to pump another, but no combination of existing devices would make such a scheme worthwhile to date.

Again for military purposes, there is the problem of the power needed to energize the flash lamp of a ruby laser. After all, there isn't always a convenient electric power socket available on the battlefield, and battery packs do not last very long when they must deliver a large amount of energy over a sustained period of time. But there may be ways around this. A well-designed system of lenses and mirrors could focus the sun's rays on a laser and thereby substitute for either a flash lamp or an electronic power supply. Indeed, solar furnaces have

already been used to melt unyielding metals and alloys—
not to mention their vaporizing of samples of hair tonic!
Then, too, radioactive isotopes might be used either to
supply electrical current for powering a flash lamp or perhaps to pump directly some yet-to-be-discovered laser.

And various techniques have been used to increase the
output of lasers themselves. One technique is called Q-
(or quality) spoiling. It tricks the laser into putting out
more energy than it would naturally give.

In Q-spoiling one of the real end mirrors of the laser rod
is temporarily removed and replaced with another some
distance away. The light wave encounters a rod seemingly
much longer than it really is. Energy builds up to fill
this fun-house distortion of the real rod. Its Q has been
"spoiled" by the removal of the real mirror. Then, as
the energy builds up, the real mirror is replaced, so that
the tuned quality of the rod is restored. By now, though,
the laser has built up a great deal of surplus energy to fill
a supposedly much longer rod, and all this energy bursts
out as a much more intense pulse than one could reasonably have hoped to achieve under normal conditions.

Thus, engineers are on their way to making lasers that
will be at once more powerful and more efficient. This
work should, by its very nature, help dispel some of the
cooling problems, since with more power coming out of
the business end of the laser, there will be less left over
to heat up the apparatus and require refrigeration.

But there is a bigger problem than any of these. The
laser beam is still just a beam of light. And, like light, it is
easily scattered or obscured by fog, rain, or clouds. Furthermore, what happens to our solar furnace when the sun
doesn't shine? Actually, even on a clear day, the effective
range of a laser is measured in feet, not in miles, because
of the absorption of its beam by the atmosphere.

Since modern war is not a game that is ever called off on account of rain, the problem of absorption by water vapor and other components of the atmosphere is a tough one to solve.

A fellow once said that if you can't lick 'em, join 'em. Then another fellow added that if you can't lick 'em and they won't let you join 'em—get away from them. And that's just what the Air Force is doing with the laser.

Is the earth's atmosphere a problem? Then get the laser out of the atmosphere.

ANTIMISSILE LASERS?

The first steps toward a workable laser weapons system are already being taken by the Air Force. The project involves operating lasers first at high altitudes on earth and later perhaps from orbiting space stations or even from antimissile missiles.

An old recipe for rabbit stew begins, "First catch a rabbit." Similarly, the Air Force's plan for destroying ballistic missile warheads starts off with finding the warhead. The notification that a missile is on the way would come from our Ballistic Missile Early Warning System. This is a network of three huge radar stations, their antennas standing like grotesque billboards and bubbles against lonely northern skies. One station is near Fairbanks, Alaska; another, near Thule in Greenland; and a third, on the wild moorland of northern England near Fylingdales.

The BMEWS radars send their warning signals over cables and special radio links to a computer control center where the signals are analyzed and ballistic missiles distinguished from astronomical bodies or other objects such as our own aircraft. BMEWS will give about twenty minutes advance warning of a ballistic missile attack.

The next step would be for a high-powered microwave

tracking radar to lock onto the missile's nose cone, so that the radar would continuously give rough positional information.

Then the tracking radar would align an optical radar with the target that would use a laser to establish the range. This method of target acquisition corresponds to the astronomer's system of using a wide-field telescope to locate a star and then changing to a high-power narrow-field telescope to study it.

The optical radar would give precise range, elevation and azimuth (or horizontal bearing) information to a control computer, which in turn would zero in the final powerful laser—the laser that would destroy the missile by burning a vulnerable part of the nose cone.

This brings up the question of how vulnerable is a ballistic missile's nuclear warhead? First of all, let's assume we are talking about a warhead carrying a hydrogen bomb. American warheads like those on the Minuteman missile have the destructive force of 700,000 to 800,000 tons of TNT. The warheads of the Soviet T-2 missile are undoubtedly larger, but their destructive force is probably not much over a megaton (1,000,000 tons of TNT).

The hydrogen-bomb or fusion reaction makes use of deuterium, a heavy form of hydrogen having one proton and one neutron in its nucleus. There are three nuclear-fusion or thermonuclear reactions in the bomb:

In the first, two deuterium atoms, or deuterons, unite (or fuse) to form helium-3 and a neutron. This reaction is accompanied by a release of energy.

In the second, two deuterons unite to form a tritium nucleus and a proton. Tritium is a radioactive isotope of hydrogen with one proton and two neutrons in its nucleus. Tritium has a half-life of twelve years.

In the third reaction a tritium nucleus and a deuteron

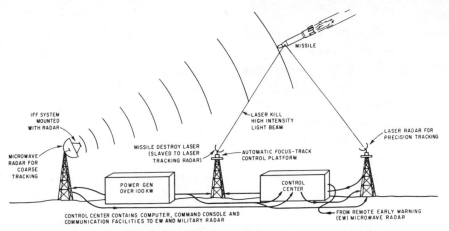

Proposed laser defense system against intercontinental ballistic missiles *(Electronics)*

combine to form helium-4 and a neutron with a release of energy.

The thermonuclear reactions occur only when the deuterium is raised to a temperature of about one million degrees centigrade. Such temperatures are achieved in the hydrogen bomb by simultaneous application of heat and pressure. This is achieved by implosion (inward explosion) of an atomic bomb.

Now, an atomic or nuclear-fission explosion occurs when a fissionable material is present in a so-called critical mass. The arming and fusing circuits of an atomic bomb involve bringing together two pieces of fissionable material such as plutonium or uranium-235 sharply to create that critical mass.

In American weapons, the components of the critical mass are attached to plungers that are driven forward by the action of squibs or small explosive charges set off in regular sequence by the electronic fusing and arming circuits.

Against such a device, even laser pinpricks applied at

vulnerable points could be highly effective: squibs could be fired prematurely, timing circuits disabled, and the bomb either predetonated harmlessly in the stratosphere (unlikely) or disabled so as to fall harmlessly to earth (more likely).

But observation of Russian equipment would lead one to believe that they tend to eschew complex electromechanical gadgetry in favor of simple, rugged, and reliable mechanisms. Accordingly, they probably use a windup clock mechanism and a powerful coiled spring to drive the plungers forward.

Furthermore, the Russians most likely use "dead-man" firing mechanisms that will set off a bomb on contact with earth even if the main fusing and arming system is disabled. Thus, their nuclear warheads may be less vulnerable to pinpricks than ours, all of which doubtless explains our extremely high interest in developing lasers capable of literally vaporizing a re-entering nose cone and the apparent unwillingness of our military leaders to place too high a value on laser weapons until such a level of performance has been demonstrated. All this presupposes development of elaborate and complex equipment for computing the position of the nose cone, swinging the laser quickly into position, focusing it precisely on target, and holding it in position long enough for it to do its damage.

The problem of decoys, the phony missile nose cones shot out to draw the fire of antimissile missiles such as the Army's Nike Zeus or Nike X, would not invalidate the laser killing concept, since a powerful and accurate laser defense system could, in the time available, burn up the real missile nose cone along with its decoys. But some means would have to be provided to avoid destroying friendly satellites or other vehicles. This could be an IFF (identification-friend-or-foe) system attached to the microwave tracking radar. IFF is an automatic, coded reply system consisting of an interrogator on the radar and an answerer (called a transponder) on the vehicle which combine to give the challenge and countersign whenever a friendly vehicle comes within range of the radar.

Development of the optical radar is already under way. At Cloudcroft, New Mexico, only a few miles from Trinity Site where a steel chain fence still encloses the acres of glazed sand melted by the first atomic bomb, the land rises a mile high from the hot yucca and mesquite-speckled desert of the Tularosa Basin.

Here on a mountain peak where the air is clear, dry, and crisp, the Air Force has installed a giant 48-inch tracking telescope with a laser transmitter attached to it. On the same precision mount are twin 15-inch visual acquisition telescopes. The system will be able to cover an area of 300 square feet at a range of 100 miles and to locate an object within ten feet.

The Air Force is going to use the optical radar to track Discoverer satellites. These satellites are launched periodically from California's Vandenberg Air Force base to make polar orbits around the earth.

But because there are not always high mountains convenient to cities or other vulnerable points requiring protection from intercontinental ballistic missiles, other operational sites must be found. As I said at the beginning of this chapter, it might be possible to mount antimissile lasers on orbiting space platforms; these lasers would be radar-controlled and could be pumped by solar energy, but there would be the problem of making the platform stable enough for accurate focusing of the laser. Then, too, lasers could be carried by interceptor or antimissile rockets, the optical pumping supplied by the kind of chemical flash powders photographers used in the days before flash bulbs.

As matters stand, then, bursts from present-day lasers might be too few and far between to do much damage to a nuclear warhead. High-powered lasers today require four or five minutes between bursts to permit the storing of energy for the next blast and the cooling of the laser head. If we were able to operate them from outer space where the sun's rays could provide optical pumping and the intense cold would dissipate the heat, the laser might be made a more effective weapon. A partial answer to reducing energy storage time is the so-called Gatling-gun laser in which six laser rods are arranged in a circle, as are the firing chambers of a revolver cylinder.

But even if all the problems of energy, heat, stability, and atmospheric absorption were solved, there would remain the factor of what antilaser countermeasures an enemy might employ. He could lay down a smoke screen in the path of the laser beam. Or he might rely on a highly polished surface to deflect the beam away from his nuclear warhead; reflection techniques are currently being studied as a possible means of protecting men and equipment from nuclear bomb blast temperatures up to 3,000 degrees Fahrenheit. Nevertheless, the effectiveness of a polished surface against a laser beam is open to question. Certainly any tarnishing of the surface of a polished reflector would allow the laser to begin its work and perhaps destroy the target, and when a missile nose cone re-entered the earth's atmosphere the fiery heat generated would be sure to tarnish even the brightest reflecting surface.

THE POWER OF A LASER

Just what capabilities does a laser have for burning

missile skins and other metallic objects? It is obvious that packing a lot of energy into a narrow beam of light should make it possible to spew out destruction at a speed of 186,000 miles a second. But how much destruction?

Lasers can produce temperatures in target materials many times hotter than the temperature of the surface of the sun itself. In one test, a laser beam impinged upon the surface of a sample of stainless steel. Not only did it form a crater on the surface where the metal was completely vaporized or blown away; it also caused damage far below the surface. Beneath the crater, the steel had melted and then solidified again to form brittle cast steel. And even below that, the steel had been partly annealed.

Laser energy is measured in *joules*, a unit of energy in the metric system. Energy is defined as the ability to do work. As such it is related to power, which is the rate of doing work. For example, the horsepower originally meant the amount of work a horse could do in a day. It was an eighteenth century advertising gimmick used to compare the effectiveness of the steam engines then coming into use with the horses then used to do the bulk of man's work.

A joule may be defined as a watt-second (product of watts times seconds) or a coulomb-volt (product of coulombs times volts): the expressions are exactly equivalent. The coulomb is a measure of electrical charge. It is equal to about 6,250 million billion electrons. A 50-joule laser can set fire to paper or wood up to a mile away: the razor-blade-piercing, balloon-popping demonstration model put out only 20 joules. Already one company is selling commercially a 350-joule laser. The larger unit can cut through a ⅛-inch steel plate. Another firm has demonstrated a 500-joule laser that can, it is claimed, cut through a ¼-inch steel

Beam from a 500-joule laser blasts through a steel girder (Raytheon)

plate. The 500-joule laser uses a ruby rod 12 inches long and ⅜-inch in diameter. It is pumped by an array of eight electronic flash lamps, and has to be cooled with liquid nitrogen.

And lasers potentially more powerful than the ruby-rod type have been proposed. One laser would depend on conversion of hydrogen between two energy states. Its output would be at 85,000 Å in the far-infrared region of the spectrum, but optical lenses could still focus its beam down to one centimeter in diameter. Developmental models are expected to deliver a beam with a temperature of 1,000 dgrees Fahrenheit into a 200-foot evacuated tube. Because of atmospheric absorption, such a laser would have to be operated from at least 100,000 feet in space, and would therefore be installed on an orbiting space platform or in the gondola of a Stratoscope-type balloon. For within the earth's atmosphere, its range would be less than one mile.

Since this laser would require at least a million watts of power, it would have to be powered by a nuclear source. The laser capsule would have to be at least ten feet in diameter and thirty feet long. The nuclear power source would be installed on an outrigger.

And a firm is developing a laser to deliver one billion joules. They won't say much about it except that the laser material will be a solid and that the pumping scheme is unorthodox.

But just how does a laser burn? Its cutting action has been described as a localized explosion. For example, if a one-joule laser beam is focused on a sheet of carbon paper and the pulse is of long duration, the laser only chars the paper. But when the duration of the pulse is reduced, say, to one microsecond or one millionth of a second, a snap is heard as the beam strikes the paper. The snap is caused by gases trying to escape.

Similarly, in cutting metals, long pulses allow the heat to dissipate itself over the target surface, thus reducing the cutting action. But rapid, high-peak-power pulses chip away triphammer fashion at the surface, each pulse vaporizing part of the target explosively.

These effects have led some scientists to believe that a laser beam could set up a highly destructive shock wave ahead of a re-entering missile nose cone. Others feel that radiation pressure alone could deflect missiles at some point in their trajectory.

LASERS UNDER THE SEA

The laser may prove to be a decisive weapon not only in outer space but also on our second front, inner space. Inner space or hydrospace are terms used to day to describe the vast, unknown region under the mighty oceans that cover two-thirds of the earth's surface.

Here is an area twice as great as that over which man has ever trod. It encompasses mountains higher than the Himalayas and gorges many times deeper than the Grand Canyon; desert wastelands and dense jungles. Through it flow mighty rivers—the Gulf Stream and the Humboldt Current—and in its depths dwell grotesque creatures whose form and habits stretch man's imagination.

Of this unknown world it can no longer be said: "Man marks the earth with ruin; his control stops with the shore."

In any future war, the battles fought beneath the watery plain would be as decisive, perhaps more so, than those fought on the surface, in the earth's atmosphere, or even in outer space.

The invention of the nuclear-propelled submarine freed submariners from the need of surfacing periodically to recharge the electrical batteries formerly used to power the submerged craft. Nuclear-powered submarines have already gone under the polar ice pack to the North Pole and traveled completely around the world while submerged.

The so-called "Albacore" hull, named for the first submarine to employ the design, makes it possible for both nuclear-powered and conventionally powered submarines to travel as fast as, if not faster than, some of the most rapid surface vessels; these submarines are maneuvered in three dimensions, as is an airplane.

ANTISUBMARINE LASERS?

There is one major drawback in undersea operations that hinders both attacker and defender, hunter and quarry. For the most part, submarines must operate almost blind. In clear waters such as the Arctic Ocean or Caribbean sea, an underwater television system using natural illumination might have a range of, say, 150 yards at relatively shallow depths; marine scientists have reported experimental light transmission (one way only) to some 2,500 feet. Of course, radar works only when the submarine is on the surface.

Therefore, for contact or "visual" navigation, such as avoiding underwater objects and for finding enemy craft, submarines must rely on sonar (*sound navigation and ranging*). Sonar works something like radar: a pulse of high-frequency inaudible sound (between 20 and 300 kilocycles per second in most sets) is sent out, bounces off an underwater object or hostile submarine, and returns to echo on a special cathode-ray tube.

But sonar suffers serious limitations. Some marine life, such as shrimp, whales, and dolphins, make noises that are picked up by sonar receivers, and generate false signals. Because sonar "antennas" called transducers produce beams nowhere near so narrow as those of radar sets, sonar cannot give as well defined a picture of what goes on underwater as radar can of what goes on above water. Furthermore, the sonar beam is broadened or scattered by sea water, thereby making definition even poorer. Schools of small fish, plankton, and silt help to compound the scattering problem. Sound waves do not always travel in a straight path under water as radar usually does in air. A difference in the saltiness of sea water can cause a sonar beam to bend and make a target appear where it is not.

Then, too, because most submarines have detectors capable of receiving enemy sonar signals, by the very use of its sonar a stalking submarine can give away its own presence long before the sonar will reveal the whereabouts of its quarry. And not only submarines have these detectors: there are also chains of underwater listening stations equipped with hydrophones designed specifically to spot intruding submarines. We have such chains guarding the Atlantic and Pacific Ocean approaches to our shores, as well as a chain in the Aleutian Islands off Alaska and another across the Straits of Greenland. Presumably the Russians have taken similar defensive measures.

There are also mines that are detonated when hit by a sonar beam and torpedoes designed to home in on enemy sonar.

Clearly, we need better underwater eyes than sonar is able to provide. So enters, we hope, the laser.

We mentioned laser radar in connection with possible use in defense against intercontinental ballistic missile nose cones. Similarly, a coherent, highly collimated beam of light (or series of closely spaced light pulses) could be made to scan repetitively one line at a time across the target area underseas. The light bounced back from objects in the area would be picked up by a phototube and the signals displayed on a special cathode-ray tube, not unlike a conventional television picture tube.

The needle-sharp laser beam would paint a picture in which every object in the target area would be precisely defined in size, shape, and location. Furthermore, you could also see at a glance how far away each object was.

Laser radars of this type have already been developed. The laser beam can be swept rapidly across the target area by action of electrical signals on a special crystal through which the laser beam passes. Such a crystal might be made of potassium dihydrogen phosphate (KDP) or ammonium dihydrogen phosphate (ADP). Strangely enough both these materials have, at one time or another, found use in conventional sonar transducers. One scientist is working on a special ceramic material intended both to replace the end mirrors of the laser cavity and to accomplish scanning.

Transmitting a laser beam underwater involves none of the problems of a radar beam. All that is needed is a tiny porthole. The laser works underwater (with limited range), in the atmosphere, or in outer space.

Incidentally, even though radar requires a two-way range in order to send a signal out and get the echo back, it is only the one-way range that is important in communications. And one important use of an underwater laser system would be submarine-to-submarine communication in which the needle-sharp laser beam would ensure privacy. Today such sub-to-sub communications are sent by sonar, whose beam diffuses widely for all to hear.

But a laser beam is only a light beam. A very special light beam, of course: intense, coherent, and highly collimated or parallel. But it is still light none the less. And sea water, as every skin diver knows, quickly absorbs even the intense light of the sun itself.

Furthermore, sea water has a blue-green cast, more or less, its color averaging out to around 5,300 Å.

THE ELUSIVE BLUE-GREEN LASER

Since most visible-light lasers today operate in the deep-red region, conditions underwater couldn't be worse as far as color is concerned. The laser beam's color is practically the complement of the color of sea water. As a result, the sea water acts as an absorbing filter and cuts the intensity of the beam most severely.

What is needed is a blue-green laser, and the Navy has a score of companies off on an underwater treasure hunt for just such a device.

Meanwhile, many studies are going on to find out what would be the capabilities of a blue-green laser radar underwater should one be found that has practical possibilities.

The Navy did some testing at David Taylor Model Basin in Carderock, Maryland, just northwest of Washington, D.C. Here the Navy has a large tank where they check out proposed hull design in scale-model form before starting actual construction of a ship.

Navy scientists took two 5-inch-diameter submarine periscopes, one to couple signals into the basin, the other to couple signals out. They used a radar transmitter with a ruby laser as its heart. The laser had only seven hundredths of a joule of energy. This corresponded to a peak pulse power output of 200 watts. The scientists found the maximum range was about 150 feet.

Then, to simulate a blue-green laser, they replaced the ruby-rod laser with a powerful white light and used filters to measure transmission of this incoherent light at about 4,900, 5,220 and 5,650 Å. From these data, the scientists estimated that a blue-green (5,300 Å) laser equivalent to the ruby laser previously used would have a range of some 1,000 feet.

Another group has been putting filters in front of a 250-watt mercury arc lamp and using a system of lenses and parabolic reflectors to get a narrow beam. They have been bouncing signals back and forth in an eight-foot-long tank of green-dyed tap water. From their work, they estimate a one-way underwater laser range of 3,000 feet. They also have suggested a name for an underwater optical detection system—again an acronym: Vedar. It stands for *visible energy detection and ranging*.

There are two approaches to finding a blue-green laser. One is to try to discover a material that will lase at or about 5,300 Å. Many fluorescent substances, both inorganic and organic, are under investigation, but no success has thus far been reported. A second approach is to take the output of a laser operating in the near-infrared range and double it to bring it up to the blue-green optical range.

One such attempt uses a glass laser doped with the rare-earth neodymium. Its basic output is at 10,600 Å in the near-infrared region. The neodymium laser uses one stationary reflector and one spinning reflector. The spinning reflector produces a Q-spoiling effect to build up the intensity of the pulse.

After going first through a filter to cut out visible light and then through a focusing lens, the infrared beam goes through a nonlinear crystal of either KDP or ADP that doubles its frequency (halves its wavelength). The result is a beam at 5,300 Å which then has to go through another lens for recollimation (making the beam parallel) and another filter to absorb any infrared radiation that managed to sneak through.

This so-called harmonic or frequency-doubling laser has between 1 and 3 percent efficiency. For example, for every 300,000 watts in, approximately 10,000 watts go out, still a substantial amount of peak pulse power. The doubler has the needle-sharp beam typical of a laser. It has a special value in that its actual frequency can be shifted, depending upon the type of glass in which the neodymium is dissolved. Thus a submarine might carry slightly different laser rods for use in the North Atlantic Ocean than in the Pacific Ocean because of the different colors of the waters.

The developers of this system suggest that it may be used not only for the precise outlining of a target and for submarine-to-submarine communications but also for guiding torpedos and unmanned submarines (underwater missiles?) and for detecting mines without triggering the antisonar pickup arrangement that we mentioned earlier.

LASER SIDE ARMS?

There have been many other military uses suggested for the laser. One of the more farfetched is the so-called laser squirt gun. This would be a portable antipersonnel weapon to be carried as a side arm. It would use a chemical compound to provide the light to pump a ruby laser. A small mechanical pump would inject the chemical ingredients into the laser head where they would unite, flare up, and optically pump the ruby rod. A lens would focus the output sharply for burning. Needless to say, many technical breakthroughs will be needed before such a device becomes practical. But we know the Army has a project under way at New York University in which lasers are used to kill small animals, which are then dissected to determine the exact physiological damage caused.

INFRARED COMMUNICATIONS

But currently laser applications are preparing for the battlefield. One objective is secure infrared communications. An infrared laser would transmit a narrow beam of invisible light onto a phototube receiver. The beam might be interrupted to transmit the familiar dots and dashes of the Morse Code or the five-bit combinations of mark and space that operate remote automatic typewriters when a teletypewriter code is employed. The laser beam might even carry voice communications. It would be secure from enemy interception unless the enemy knew exactly where the beam was located and approximately what infrared wavelength was being used.

LASER RANGE FINDER

The Army and the North Atlantic Treaty Organization forces are already purchasing another laser instrument for use in the field. This is the laser range finder.

Finding the distance from a mortar, howitzer, or field gun to a selected enemy target is a difficult and often dangerous task. But it is necessary to determine the proper elevation of the gun and setting of the fuses on the shells. With larger guns, such as the 11-inch atomic cannon or large-caliber naval rifles that use semifixed ammunition, you must know the range to determine how many powder bags to put into the breech behind the shell.

One way of finding the range is to survey and plot a base line that runs parallel to the enemy lines and that either includes your guns or has a known offset from them. Triangulation provides the range after the angle between the base line and a line to the target is ascertained at two known points on the base line. These measurements are taken with an optical telescope mounted on a kind of protractor. But in modern war, lines are fluid; besides, artillery surveyors are prime targets for enemy sharpshooters.

If, then, you can't survey in a base line, you have to take a base line with you. Hence the optical range finder uses a pair of telescopes mounted a couple of feet apart. There are also battlefield radar sets, but they are relatively bulky and hard to maintain under field conditions.

In any event, because you seldom get the range right the first time, you have to bracket the target with "longs" and "shorts," and have a forward observer in a plane or on the front lines watching the effects of the bombardment and radioing back the results. Meanwhile, you are giving away the position of your own guns to the enemy

Rifle-like laser range finder fires light beam from long barrel; shorter barrel receives reflected light pulses. Telescopic sight is for aiming (Hughes)

and subjecting yourself to counterbattery fire. In these days when mortar-detecting radar can track a shell back to its origin, counterbattery fire can be effective indeed. And the forward observer's spot is not all beer and skittles either: we lose all too many promising young artillery officers that way.

A laser range finder is put on a rifle stock, and may be aimed without the use of a tripod or other mount. It weighs about 2 pounds in all, including both the rifle portion and a backpack. The rifle portion consists of the laser transmitter—a ruby rod and flash lamp, a two-foot-long optical telescope used for focusing the beam, an optical sighting telescope, and the receiver, which is a photocell.

The backpack contains the batteries, electronic pulsing circuits, the receiver amplifiers, and readout system. The digital readout system gives the range directly in numbers that appear in little windows like those on a desk calculator or the odometer of your car.

One laser range finder has determined range within fifteen feet while ranging on buildings seven miles away. When used from a helicopter flying at one thousand feet, it determined range up to 11,000 yards. Its maximum range under ideal conditions and over a path where the curvature of the earth does not intervene would be about 60 miles.

The laser range finder is not restricted to use on the battlefield. It might also be used at sea or mounted in the nose of an aircraft to provide information necessary to employ folding-fin rockets. It has potential commercial applications in surveying and mapping over water or chasms. Its ground range is, of course, limited by line-of-sight and weather conditions.

Peaceful Applications in Outer Space

Of course, as we have seen, the true milieu of the laser is outer space. Here no clouds or rain can absorb its power, and here its precision as a ranging device may make the difference between success and failure of a mission. And our Space Agency has been quick to recognize its potential.

LASER RADAR

One of the first laser tests was made at Wallops Island,

Virginia—a long, low, pine-barren sand pit where the Old Dominion looks out over miles of foamy surf at the Atlantic Ocean.

At the Space Agency installation scientists used a pulsed ruby laser to bounce light off an orbiting satellite 1,500 kilometers away. The satellite was the NASA S-66 Polar Ionosphere Satellite. It was launched from our Pacific Missile Range into an orbit that carried it over each Pole to measure conditions in the earth's upper atmosphere. The satellite was equipped with a panel made up of a mosaic of 360 half-inch reflecting cubes. These were specially designed to attain the best possible reflection of ruby-laser light. The laser ranging system was able to pinpoint the satellite position within 50 feet.

From tests like this are coming an impressive number of laser instruments for satellite and spacecraft communications and navigation.

SPACE COMMUNICATIONS

The next United States manned space shot will be part of the Gemini project that will carry two astronauts in a single space capsule. The object of Project Gemini is to perfect techniques for satellite rendezvous and docking— first to orbiting rocket booster bodies and later to other manned spacecraft.

One of the Gemini astronauts will aim a small hand-carried gallium-arsenide laser transmitter at a receiver on the ground at a location marked by a flare. He will then transmit a 30-second voice message over the laser beam to test its effectiveness for space-to-earth communications.

DOPPLER LASER RADAR

Rendezvous of two satellites will require precise knowledge of the closing speed with which they are approaching each other. Presently the best way to ascertain this is with doppler radar in which a continuous microwave beam is sent out and bounced off a moving target. Doppler radar sets are widely used by police departments to measure the speed of motorists. There is a difference in frequency between the transmitted and reflected signals that depends upon how fast the target is moving relative to the transmitter.

In doppler speedmeters, a radar beam is speeded up by the speed of an approaching vehicle off which it is reflected. Since wavelength remains constant, the echo bounced off the car returns to the radar set at a higher frequency than the signal leaving the radar set. The difference between these two frequencies is called the beat note. It is proportional to the speed of the approaching vehicle.

The doppler laser radar would be able to determine closing speed ten thousand times more accurately than a typical microwave radar. It would be able to measure satellite closing speed from three miles a second down to one-thousand inch per second!

The doppler laser would use a helium-neon continuous-wave laser (11,530 Å). With only one-watt output, its range in space would be about 1,000 miles. Furthermore, even a ten-watt unit would weight only about 15 pounds.

RADAR ALTIMETER

After Project Gemini comes Project Apollo in which a space capsule carrying three astronauts will be shot into orbit around the moon. Then while one astronaut remains aboard the moon-circling mother spaceship, the other two astronauts will board the "bug," or LEM (lunar excursion module), which will be launched from the main Apollo capsule and descend to the lunar surface where the astronaut pair plan to spend a long weekend.

It now seems likely that at least some of the later moon bugs will be equipped with laser altimeters to measure altitude and closing speed precisely as the LEM approaches the moon's surface.

Since the bug will back into the face of the moon, the altimeter will have to see through the craft's exhaust. And a rocket exhaust is actually a plasma or plume of electrically conducting ionized gas. Such a plasma is impervious to many radio and microwave frequencies but not to laser beams.

The ability to penetrate a plasma sheath is also important in communicating with spacecraft re-entering the earth's atmosphere. When a space capsule hurtles into the atmosphere, air friction heats the outside of the craft almost to incandescence, and in so doing ionizes the air around it, making the air electrically conducting, thereby creating the plasma sheath that cuts off normal radio communications, and caused several minutes of worldwide apprehension during the final moments of some of the Project Mercury manned space shots.

The ability of the laser to penetrate this sheath of silence has led to high interest in lasers for spacecraft and satellite communications.

LASER GYROSCOPES

And finally there is midcourse spacecraft navigation. Now, all missile flights are divided into three phases: boost, midcourse, and terminal. In the boost phase they are aimed and their powered flight guided from the ground. In the terminal phase they may use altimeters such as those just described. In between, they rely on stellar or inertial guidance or a combination of both.

In inertial guidance, the position of the vehicle is determined by measuring its displacement constantly in comparison to a fixed point in space. The fixed point in space is determined by means of an inertial platform, or so-called "stable table." The position of the inertial platform, which is the heart of the vehicle's inertial-guidance system, is fixed in space by the action of three gyroscopes.

A toy gyroscope illustrates how these gyros are used in inertial guidance. When such a toy, consisting of a relatively heavy wheel spinning on a pivot, is set into motion, it has a strong tendency to stand erect as long as it is spinning rapidly. In fact, if you try to knock it over, it will restore itself to an erect position by curling around in a spiral fashion.

If you set three gyros spinning around axes that are all perpendicular to one another, one or more of the gyros will tend to be knocked over by any force or combination of forces applied to the three-gyro system.

An inertial platform consists of just such a three-gyro system so arranged that the restoring force exerted by the gyros generates an electrical signal that is then fed back and used to keep the platform stable with respect to a fixed point in space.

In addition, an inertial-guidance system has three sensing devices, called accelerometers, each at right angles to the others. Each accelerometer senses any acceleration of the vehicle in its particular direction and puts out a corresponding electrical signal. When this signal is passed successively through two electronic circuits called integrators, the resulting output signal tells how far the vehicle has gone in that direction. The three signals together, along with the inertial platform used as a position reference, determine where the vehicle is in space at all times.

Today our intercontinental ballistic missiles and smaller missiles, space probes and spacecraft, Polaris submarines and even manned aircraft, all use inertial-guidance systems.

But we mentioned that the gyroscopes have to be spinning rapidly in order to function, and there's the rub. Because friction slows down even the best mechanical gyros after a while, the stable platform ceases to be stable. Then the system has to be corrected, sometimes by sighting in on the stars, as is done aboard Polaris-carrying submarines.

But engineers may have come up with an idea for a laser "gyroscope" that never needs to be corrected. This gyro doesn't spin at all; a laser beam rotates instead. It uses a helium-neon gas laser which, as you remember, can emit a beam of coherent infrared light from each end. The laser is situated midway on one side of a one-meter square. There are 45-degree mirrors at each corner of the square that rotate the beam from one end of the laser in a clockwise direction and rotate the beam from the other end of the laser in a counterclockwise direction. Now, if no force acts on the laser gyro, the frequencies of the two beams are equal, and no beat or frequency difference is detected when the beams are passed through combining optics to photodetectors.

But if the device is rotated, one beam increases in frequency while the other decreases, since the speed of light is constant although the rotation alters the path lengths. This change in frequency arising from mechanical motion is like the radar doppler effect used in police speedmeters. The beat note corresponds to the rate at which the laser gyro is rotated.

Here we are not really measuring the angle through which the apparatus is turned but rather the rate at which it is turned, or its *angular velocity*. To obtain the actual turning angle from a measurement of angular velocity, it is necessary to perform the calculus operation of integra-

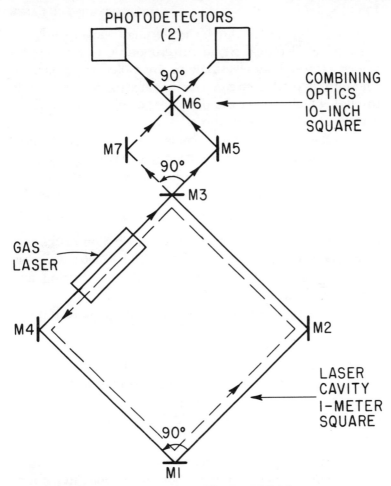

PHOTODETECTORS
(2)

90°

M6

COMBINING
OPTICS
IO-INCH
SQUARE

M7   M5

90°

M3

GAS
LASER

M4   M2

LASER
CAVITY
I-METER
SQUARE

90°

MI

M3 IS PARTIALLY TRANSPARENT MIRROR
M6 IS TRANSPARENT MIRROR
ALL OTHER MIRRORS ARE IOO-PERCENT REFLECTIVE

Laser gyroscope can be used for midcourse guidance of space
vehicles *(Electronics)*

tion. This operation can be performed conveniently by passing the electrical signal corresponding to the angular velocity through an electronic circuit called an integrator. The output of this circuit corresponds to the total angle through which the gyro, and hence the vehicle upon which it is mounted, has been turned.

Thus the laser gyro corresponds to an electromechanical device known as a rate (or velocity) gyroscope. One ring-laser gyro has achieved a resolution of two degrees of turning per minute.

THE LASER IN INDUSTRY

It may seem a far cry from space navigation to the machine shop, but the laser has industrial functions: lasers have proved useful in welding metals and cutting and machining both metals and other materials.

No one is seriously considering replacing the drill press, engine lathe, or milling machine with a laser, for that would be like setting out to paint your house with an artist's palette or carving your Sunday roast with a Number 10 scalpel. And for the same reason, no one is thinking about using lasers to replace oxyacetelene torches for metal cutting or electric welding sets for joining metals for the same reasons.

MICROWELDING AND MACHINING

But there are many precision jobs to be done in modern technology, especially in the electronics and aerospace industries, and the laser is a very precise tool indeed.

Transistors are already the size of a pinhead, and each requires up to three precisely located welded connections. In one test, a laser welded a one-mil-diameter wire to a transistor chip in only a millionth of a second, faster and more reliably than conventional thermal-compression welders can work.

Laser piercing a 1/16-inch-thick sapphire crystal in one millisecond. Surface temperature is 2800 degrees C. *(Electronics)*

In the field of microelectronics, complete electronic circuits containing the equivalent of several transistors and other parts are being diffused into and deposited upon blocks of silicon small enough to pass through the eye of a large needle. Some of these microcircuits require a dozen welds, and others intricate machining as well. Here are more potential jobs for the laser.

A laser has welded two wires each only 0.004-inch in diameter to make a copper-Constantan thermocouple—and it wasn't even necessary to strip the insulation off the wires first!

In another test a 7⅞-inch ruby-rod laser welded two pieces of oxygen-free high-conductivity copper each 0.005 by 0.060-inch. And the pieces of copper remained sandwiched between two pieces of glass during the welding operation.

Lasers have melted or vaporized 21 varieties of metals both common and exotic: tin, tungsten, columbium, molybdenum, zirconium, and others of interest to the aerospace industries. Melting points ranged from 200 to 3,410 degrees centigrade and boiling points from 1,000 to 6,000 degrees C.

Not only can lasers melt, cut, and weld difficult-to-handle metal alloys coming into use in the space age; they can also cut nonmetallic materials too brittle to be cut by conventional means, such as ceramics. And they have been put to work on electrical insulating materials, sapphire crystals used to protect solar cells of communications satellites from the radiation of the Van Allen belts, and even diamonds.

INSPECTION AND PHOTOGRAPHY

Since ordinary white light suffers from chromatic aberration in which some color components are bent more than others in passing through a lens or prism, the monochromaticity, or single color, of the laser beam suits it peculiarly for other industrial uses also. It offers vast possibilities in precision inspection of mechanical parts. It is being used in making diffraction gratings of extremely fine-ruled parallel lines for optical and X-ray spectrum analysis.

Lasers are also useful in making diffusion masks for microcircuits. These masks must be made with utmost precision, since they are used to form the silicon-dioxide patterns around which go impurities that are diffused into the silicon block to produce an array of transistors, diodes, and other parts.

And lasers can be used in industrial high-speed photography, especially in Schliering, or knife-edge photography used to visualize shock-wave patterns in hypersonic wind tunnels.

LASER COMPUTERS

Lasers may help automatic digital computers over a barrier that engineers once thought insurmountable: the barrier of the speed with which the electrons that make up a pulse of electrical current can travel down a wire.

Early electronic computers performed their basic operations of adding, comparing, and transferring bits of information in thousandths of seconds. They worked in the millisecond range.

Modern computers work in the submicrosecond range. They perform their basic operations in less than one millionth of a second. This improvement in operating speed has made possible solving problems that would have been impractical to solve on earlier computers.

A computer does much more work to solve a problem than you do. For example, to find the square root of a number, a computer repetitively squares all numbers in a given range until it finds the one whose square matches the number whose square root is desired.

Actually, all a computer need do is addition—subtraction is just inverse or "nines complement" addition; multiplication is only repeated addition; while division is repeated subtraction.

So, mathematically speaking, computers are not very bright. Thus, they must make up for their lack of sophistication by great speed of operation. And as man has called upon computers to solve problems of ever-increasing complexity, he has been faced with two courses of action: either build bigger and bigger computers so that the problems can be split up into many parts and each part worked on in a different portion of the machine or make computers that can do their work faster. Actually, man did a little of both, and computers have simultaneously grown larger and become faster.

This evolution of the computer has come about by finding ever faster and more reliable electronic parts. Parts had to be more reliable because the larger the machine, the more chance there is for a part to fail and cause the machine to break down. So out went the vacuum tubes and in came transistors, and then even smaller and faster transistors.

But still the question remained: How do you cope with the time it takes for a pulse of current to travel down a wire? The answer a few years ago seemed to be to stop using pulses of current and begin using microwave signals that travel at the speed of light. But if you want to keep many microwave signals from interfering with one another, you have to use special hollow cables in which the microwave signals can travel.

The smallest that engineers have been able to make these cables is about 30/1,000 of an inch in diameter. And even then there is a considerable loss of signal power in the cables. Furthermore, equipment needed to generate microwave signals is bulky and very expensive.

And so came the solution:

To get a computer to operate with the speed of light, why not use light itself? The advent of the laser made this apparently obvious answer to the problem a feasible one.

Instead of microwave cables, the optical computer uses optical fibers. It is possible to make optical fibers only one millionth of an inch in diameter; fibers one thousandth of an inch wide are commonplace. Thus an optical computer can be made many times smaller than a microwave computer—perhaps even smaller than an electric one.

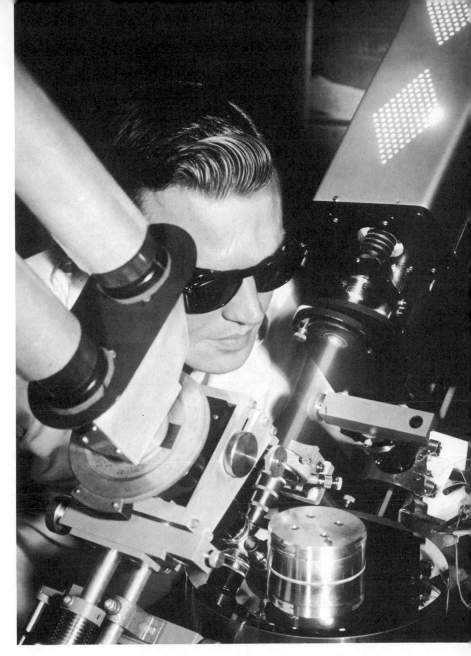

Using a laser beam to read data stored on a magnetic dial of an automatic digital computer *(Electronics)*

There is another advantage optical fibers have over either wires or microwave cables. As electrical current or a microwave signal passes down wires or cables, it loses its energy all along the way, and at some point an electronic circuit known as an amplifier has to be inserted in the line to boost the signal back up where it belongs. This is especially necessary where one signal must branch or fan out to feed many parallel lines, as is frequently the case in computer work. But with an optical computer, the amplification could become easy.

Recall that in the plastic laser a rare-earth metal such as europium provided the necessary energy transition to generate coherent light and that this rare-earth atom could be contained in a complex ring-shaped organic molecule called a chelate. The chelate molecules, in turn, could be suspended in liquid, glass, or plastic.

Now if, along the path of the computer pulse chelate molecules were suspended in the fiber optic rod and the chelate pumped to just below firing threshold, the pulse of coherent light coming down the line would cause the whole optical fiber to fire and the pulse would arrive at its destination not weakened from loss of power in the line but instead amplified.

The exciting thing about this kind of optical circuit is that its operation closely parallels the operation of the human nerve cell or neuron. The only difference is that the optical fiber can be made even smaller than a human neuron, and signals will travel along it faster than they do along a neuron.

With time and space to spare, computers would not have to be designed deterministically so that each step in their operation must be spelled out as if for an idiot child. Now there might be several paths to a single goal and the computer might be "trained" to follow one path under one set of input conditions and a different path under some other set of conditions. Circuits like this are referred to as adaptive logic, and they could permit a computer to learn a task by doing it just as a human learns.

Right now the major problem in optical computers is getting their efficiency high enough so that the power to operate them is not unduly high. But every new type of equipment reaches its peak efficiency only after months or years of engineering refinement, so doubtless the power requirement can be reduced.

In the days when the slow, old Eniac computer was being hailed as a giant brain, scientists pointed out, quite rightly, that Eniac was by no means a brain. Nor, they said, would it ever be practical to build the capacity of a human brain into a computer. Such a computer would, they asserted, have to be larger than the Empire State Building. Moreover, it would take the water of three Niagaras to cool it.

Well, the size of computers as compared to their capabilities has been shrinking all the time, and the optical computer may one day be smallest of all. Cooling would certainly not be a serious problem, if the computer were small enough so that one could dunk the whole of it in liquid helium!

LASER COMMUNICATIONS ON EARTH

Lasers may be used for short-range communications within the atmosphere as well as for over much longer distances in outer space. An injection or semiconductor-diode laser is especially easy to use for transmitting speech or music.

A system of modulation, which is the act of impressing intelligence upon any signal, called pulse-frequency modulation, is used. In this system, the rate at which the diode laser is flashed increases when the speech or music gets louder. A very simple arrangement will transmit signals with roughly the quality of a telephone line over short distances. The individual direct-current pulses that actuate the injection laser are only two-tenths of one millionth of a second wide and five amperes in magnitude.

TV BY LASER

A more complex system has been used to transmit both the sound and picture portions of a regular television signal over a laser light beam. The source of the beam was a helium-neon gas laser operating at 6,328 Å, in the deep-red region.

Experimental setup for transmitting television sound and pictures over a laser beam (*Electronics*)

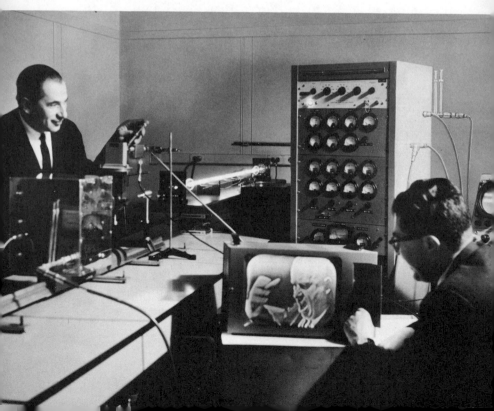

The beam was modulated by passing it through a crystal of KDP (potassium dihydrogen phosphate). Now, KDP has a very interesting optical property. When a crystal is placed in a box called a microwave cavity (with optical windows on opposite sides) and irradiated with microwave energy, it will modulate the polarization of a single-color light beam.

Polarized light has all the light rays making up a beam lined up in one direction; that is how polarized sunglasses reduce glare: by blocking out the random reflections that sparkle every which way and allowing only orderly light waves to reach your eyes.

When the KDP crystal is saturated with microwave energy; it rotates the axis of these light waves 90 degrees; with minimum energy in the crystal, there will be no rotation. Now, if at the receiving end you have an optical arrangement consisting of a quarter-wave plate and linear analyzer, you can arrange things so that when the beam is rotated 90 degrees, the maximum possible light gets through, while with no rotation of the polarized laser beam, minimum light gets through.

In the laser TV system, a television signal out of a home receiver was used to modulate a microwave signal of 3,000 megacycles per second, called a subcarrier. The modulated subcarrier was then amplified by a special type of microwave device called a traveling wave tube. This was the microwave signal that was applied to the KDP crystal.

At the receiving end, the laser beam was focused on a special microwave phototube that recovered the same microwave signal that was applied to the KDP crystal by following the rapid changes in the intensity of laser light coming through the linear analyzer.

The electrical signal from the phototube was amplified

by more traveling wave tubes and then converted back to an ordinary television signal by an electronic circuit, called a video detector, so that it could be displayed on a conventional television picture tube.

TELEPHONE SYSTEMS TO COME

As we have said, as many as 600 simultaneous telephone conversations could be carried on such a laser beam. In fact, there isn't any limit to the number of telephone conversations that can be carried on a laser beam. One beam has enough room to carry every conversation going on at one given time anywhere in the world. The only thing that limits a laser communications system is the capability of the modulator, but improvements in this type of equipment are being made.

Of course, a laser beam would have a very short range in the earth's atmosphere. But laser beams could travel in evacuated light pipes having systems of mirrors to direct the beam around corners where necessary. And a laser beam might be just the thing for getting information-packed signals to and from orbiting communications satellites such as Telstar and Relay.

Another communications application of the laser might be in telephone exchanges. Assume two telephone central offices are connected by a light pipe over which all the interoffice conversations are transmitted by a signal laser beam. The signals are demodulated, sorted out, and sent to the proper subscribers at the receiving end, while at the transmitting end the signals coming in are impressed on subcarriers that all go to modulate the single laser beam.

MEDICINE AND THE LASER

With all the concentrated energy that a laser contains,

it is understandable that the laser will have certain definite effects on living creatures.

A laser has three biological effects: the general heating effect, a specific heating effect, and the electrical effect of concentrated electromagnetic energy in the laser pulse. The electrical effect is most noticable in hemoglobin, or red blood cells, where it changes their electrical conductivity. Actually, hemoglobin is an iron chelate, and therefore the cells might be reasonably expected to absorb laser energy to a marked extent.

GENERAL HEATING

The general heating effect of the laser results when individual cells absorb energy from the laser beam. This is the same thing that occurs when you get a sunburn. The beam can cause reddening, blistering, and charring of the skin, depending upon the intensity of the laser pulse and the duration of exposure.

However, the effects are only skin deep, and the surrounding tissue and blood vessels serve to conduct away heat energy built up in the exposed cells.

But in certain parts of the body, such as the eyeballs and testes, there is minimal connection to surrounding tissue and inadequate blood supply to conduct away energy built up from local exposure to the laser beam. When these organs are exposed to a laser, severe tissue damage deep within the organs can occur, and as a result there is a distinct danger of causing blindness or sterility.

LASER BLINDING: SOME PRECAUTIONS

Pigmented tissue absorbs more energy from laser beams than does ordinary tissue. Thus, the choroid coating, or light-sensitive portion, of the inside of the eyeball could be damaged in a fraction of a second by a high-intensity laser beam.

One suggested protective device is a pair of thick, opaque goggles with a tiny hole in the lens center. The beam would have to go through this hole to reach the eye. A cap shield around the edges of the hole would give even more protection.

Should the beam enter the direct hole path, probably only the macula, or point of sharp focus on the retina, would be damaged. A victim could still see light and dark and gross objects, but his ability to focus sharply would be destroyed.

It has been suggested that narrow-band optical filters could be designed to attenuate the laser beam to safe levels while still passing sufficient light for vision. But safe exposure levels for laser beams are not yet known.

Actually, there is now no valid eye safety device except to avoid looking at the direct laser beam. Tests on rabbits to determine the harmful effects of lasers have produced severe thermal lesions in the eyes.

Never look directly into either end of a laser crystal, gas tube, or semiconductor diode. Even when a laser is turned off, it is not always safe. Some laser circuit designs permit the power supply capacitors to fire the laser flash tube even after the primary power has been turned off.

LASERS IN EYE SURGERY

Properly employed, the laser can be used, as we mentioned earlier, in delicate sight-saving eye surgery. It can weld shut a puncture or hole in the retina to correct retinal detachment.

Laser beams can also be used to scar and essentially destroy certain blood-vessel tumors in the eye. A laser can even create a new pupil in the pigmented portion of the eye, the iris, which has been blocked or pushed out of position as the result of partially unsuccessful eye surgery to remove a cataract. A laser could also be used to destroy certain tumors on the surface of the eye.

Each year thousands of persons develop retinal detachment. It starts with a hole or tear in the retina. Then the thick fluid in the eye—the vitreous humor—seeps through the hole, and pressure between the retina and choroid coating can eventually peel off the retina and cause blindness.

If discovered early, a detached retina can be spotwelded back into place by a light beam. A small scar develops where the beam burns the tissue behind the retina, and holds the retina in place.

Retinal flaws have, in the past, been treated by surgery, diathermy, or with an optical photo-coagulator. The optical photo-coagulator focused light from a xenon gas tube on the retina. But it required a treatment time of one-half to one second. And in this time the patient might blink or flinch. Sometimes several shots were necessary to get the scar in the right place.

However, with the laser an exposure of only 1/1,000 second is needed. This is faster than any movement of the eye, and only one shot is needed to get the spot in the right place. The treatment is so fast that it doesn't hurt; it can be given in the doctor's office without anesthesia. Furthermore, the equipment is compact and easy to use.

Another possible use of the laser is to sear shut small blood vessels to reduce loss of blood, and to maintain a dry or bloodless field during surgery. However, a radio-frequency scalpel has for some time been used by surgeons in such applications.

CAN LASERS TREAT CANCER?

One of the most challenging medical applications of the laser may be in treating cancer. Laser radiation has been used to destroy pigmented cells while adjacent transparent cells were left unaffected. Even transparent cells can be destroyed if tinted with a dye that is absorbed selectively only by the malignant cells.

It is believed that the laser may be effective in destroying malignant melanoma, a highly pigmented and fast-spreading form of cancer. The cancerous cells could be destroyed literally a cell at a time, with minimal damage to surrounding healthy tissue.

Thus, the potential range of applications for the laser range all the way from destroying intercontinental ballistic missiles to curing cancer. It could solve many of man's most difficult problems: navigating spaceships, making unlimited space available in overcrowded communications bands, exploring the mysteries of mass and energy, as well as handling more prosaic jobs such as welding and machining.

SIGNALING TO DISTANT GALAXIES

Lasers may also play a role in Project Ozma. Today, highly sensitive radio telescopes are scanning distant galaxies, searching for any sign of intelligible radio signals that might reveal the presence of civilized creatures on some unknown planet of a distant star whose environment might, like earth's, be hospitable to life. Project Ozma also calls for sending some elementary pulse pattern over high-powered radio transmitters beamed at distant galaxies. The pulse pattern would be one readily recognizable to any intelligent creature regardless of language—something like "shave and a haircut, two bits"—*dum diti dum dum, dit dit.*

But suppose these unknown beings had developed their science in terms of corpuscles instead of waves—as if in the seventeenth century Newton's theory of the nature of light had prevailed instead of Huygen's? Then our distant fellow creatures might have a civilization based on laser technology instead of radio.

Thus, scientists have proposed we supplement our radio broadcasts to the unknown reaches of outer space with pulses from a powerful laser beamed through a 200-inch telescope. The laser might then become our first means for communication with intelligent beings from the far reaches of outer space!

IV

CONSTRUCTION OF A LASER

Although lasers are already in use for so wide a variety of purposes, it will be some time before the average layman encounters one.

Nonetheless, there is an understandable urge to participate personally in the exciting research into the behavior and use of the laser. The boy down the block who used to play around with amateur radio or soup up his jalopy is probably thinking right now about building a laser. Indeed, as we shall see, at least one boy has already done so.

However, the laser is definitely not a toy—it is a complex scientific instrument, dangerous to build and to operate. The light from the laser can cause blindness and painful burning or possibly set fires, and the extremely high voltages used in the laser can cause electrocution.

And so it is fortunate that few boys will be able to assemble and operate a laser on their own. The parts needed are fantastically expensive and often difficult to obtain. Then, too, assembly of the laser requires consummate skill as an electronics technician—skill at least equal to that needed to build a one-kilowatt amateur radio transmitter. Later, in the story of Robert Armstrong, a boy who built a laser, you will note that his work was made possible only by the cooperation of several parts-manufacturers and with the help of several electronics engineers.

This chapter is not a cookbook recipe for building a laser. It does not give all the details of assembly and wiring. However, these steps should be evident to a skilled electronics technician, the only kind of person who could safely undertake its construction. Since the variations in the configuration of key components as made by different manufacturers could not all be described and dealt with here in adequate detail, for such information, we advise the prospective laser builder to seek detailed advice from his parts supplier.

LASERS AT THE FAIR

We anticipate then that any lasers constructed with the help of the information in this chapter will be built either by or under the close supervision of science teachers or other well-trained adult advisers.

Nevertheless, the annual high school science fairs at which the first prizes used to be won by kids who built Van de Graaff generators, Geiger-Müller counters, and cloud chambers may one day be giving top honors to budding scientists who pierce razor blades with their homemade lasers.

In fact, so many razor blades have been pierced by lasers that one scientist has suggested that the output of a laser no longer be rated in joules but rather in "Gillettes."

Robert Armstrong was fifteen, and a ninth-grade student in Monnig Junior High School in Fort Worth, Texas, when he won first place in his division of Fort Worth's science fair with a homemade laser. Robert was a straight-A student, played basketball and football, and hadn't yet begun to date when he put the laser together.

At first it looked as if the project wouldn't get off the ground. Robert was told it was impractical to think of

building a laser because of the expensive ruby crystal
needed to make one work. But he found a firm in Connecticut willing to lend him a ruby crystal valued at some
four hundred dollars. They wrapped the crystal carefully
in a package and air-mailed it to Texas. Robert was in
business.

Robert's father, an aeronautical engineer for General
Dynamics, encouraged his son's efforts, and two electronics engineers from General Dynamics and one from
KTVT, a local television station, helped out in various
ways. Robert says he worked on his laser every night
after he finished his homework and all through every
weekend from Christmas until the end of March.

He built a 4,000-volt power supply for a cluster of four
flashtubes that provided the optical pumping for his ruby
crystal.

His borrowed ruby was a cylinder one-fourth inch in
diameter and two inches long. It had, of course, been
fine-ground around its circumference and ground optically
flat on both ends, with the ends exactly parallel. Each
end was silvered.

The ruby rod with the four flashtubes clustered around
it was housed in a light-tight black metal box.

Now, Robert wasn't out to cut diamonds with his
laser or to light up the moon, but he was surprised and
gratified when his apparatus worked the first time he
tried it.

His laser emitted flashes of light each five one-
thousandths of a second long. And, for a happy ending,
the laser was able to make deep pits in the traditional
razor blade. It had an energy of one-half "Gillette"!

So in self-defense for every qualified father, favorite
uncle, science teacher and scoutmaster of a precocious,
scientifically-minded youngster, we give here the rudi-

ments of putting a laser together, or perhaps of taking one apart if things get out of hand.

THE RUBY CRYSTAL

The heart of the laser is the ruby crystal. Of course, it doesn't have to be ruby. It could be something like calcium tungstate doped with the rare-earth neodymium or any of dozens of other crystals containing rare-earth or actinide metals. But most of these other crystals put out invisible infrared light, while the ruby puts out a pretty red beam with which to impress visitors.

GROWING A RUBY BOULE

Ruby is actually sapphire with a small amount of chromium (about five hundredths of one percent) dissolved in it. And sapphire, in turn, is a single crystal of aluminum oxide.

A synthetic ruby is, therefore, made by melting aluminum oxide and chromium in a refractory crucible using electrical induction heating coils. A tiny ruby seed crystal is inserted into the crucible, and then the larger crystal that grows upon the tiny seed crystal is slowly drawn out of the glowing white-hot melt with a steady spiral motion. The principle of crystal growth is similar to that by which rock-salt crystals are grown in a supersaturated solution of salt, although salt crystals are grown at room temperature, while ruby crystals are grown at a white-hot heat.

The result of crystal growth is a ruby boule—an elongated, knobby single crystal of translucent pink material anywhere from an inch to a foot long and from ⅜ to ½ inch in diameter.

These ruby boules sell for about $100 an inch. Therefore the standard two-inch rod, one-fourth inch in diameter, bought as a boule might cost from $150 to $200. If

Pulling a calcium-tungstate crystal doped with neodymium out of a melt at 2800 degrees F. by the vertical growing process (Raytheon)

your hobby is amateur optics or lapidary, you might want to start out with a ruby boule when making a laser.

FROM BOULE TO ROD

If you are not sufficiently experienced with the rules of optics and gems, you had better pay another $200 and buy a ruby rod in finished form. Because the ruby boule is an overgrown sapphire, it is much harder than either glass or quartz. It must be cut with a diamond saw, and unless the cuts are exactly parallel, you'll have a lot of trouble later on. Then too, the crystal has to be *fine-ground* around its circumference with progressively smaller sizes of diamond grit to make the rod a true cylinder. After fine grinding, the outside of the ruby will still have a frosty appearance. But the ends of the ruby rod are really critical. They have to be *smooth ground,* that is, ground until they are completely transparent. The two ends have to be parallel within ten seconds of arc, and although skilled optical mechanics can check parallelism by looking down the rod, it is best checked out on an optical bench with a mirror system. The ends must be ground flat within one-quarter of the wavelength of sodium light, an accuracy that can be checked only with optical test flats.

And so if you don't have or know how to use an optical bench and optical test flats, you have no business messing around with a $200 ruby boule in the first place. It would be much better to buy a ruby rod.

Linde Air Products Division of Union Carbide in East Chicago, Indiana, supplies optical-quality ruby rods already cut, ground, and polished with parallel end faces. However, you still have to silver the end faces partially. The silver is applied as to a mirror but not so heavily. Actually, few ruby lasers made commercially today use silvered end faces, since such ends absorb too much of the light output of the ruby. Commercial lasers have multiple layers of special nonabsorbent dielectric coating. But these coatings are difficult to apply and are more expensive than silver.

Perkin-Elmer Corp., Electro-Optical Division, Norwalk, Connecticut, will supply pedigreed ruby rods already coated with multilayer dielectric film. What's more, because these rods have already been test-operated in a laser, you know the laser will work if you make everything else right. The pedigreed ruby rod comes complete with all performance data and test conditions but it costs nearly twice as much as an untested rod.

Choosing the Flash Lamp

The next thing to do is to select a flash lamp to pump your ruby rod.

HELICAL FLASH LAMP

You can, of course, take the lazy way out and use the classical General Electric Model 524 helical xenon-filled flash lamp like the one Maiman used in his first laser. This is the simplest configuration.

The only problem you will have is that of supporting the laser rod in the center of the helix. It is best to use a metal clamp, since the laser rod gets mighty hot in operation. The rear face of the laser can fit into a shallow recess in a metal rod that can in turn be fastened securely to the rear wall of the light-tight cylindrical metal housing.

A metal funnel can be used to hold the front face of the laser in position. The ruby rod should fit snugly into the small end of the funnel, while the wide end can be securely fastened to the front wall of the laser housing. Incidentally, this clamping arrangement for the laser rod

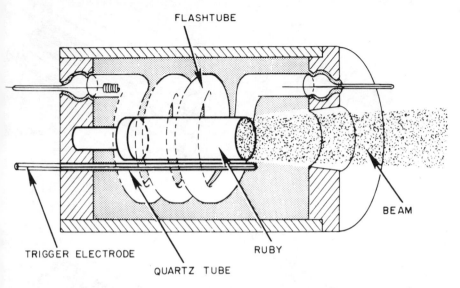

FLASHTUBE

TRIGGER ELECTRODE

QUARTZ TUBE

RUBY

BEAM

Main parts of a ruby laser using a helical flash lamp as did Maiman's original device (Hughes)

is useful irrespective of the flashtube arrangement finally selected.

The quartz flashtube rests against the sides of the cylindrical laser housing. You can improve the efficiency of your laser by polishing the inside of the laser housing. Of course, you can make the laser and helical flashtube assembly work even without a metal housing. You might use four laboratory ring stands with clamps to hold the ruby rod and flashtube in position, but this arrangement is both awkward and inefficient, since much of the optical pumping energy is lost, and it is a darned nuisance to have the flash lamp going off under your nose every few minutes.

FLASH-LAMP CLUSTER

A simple and effective technique is to use four linear flash lamps the way Robert Armstrong did. You make a cluster of flash lamps around the laser rod, then wrap

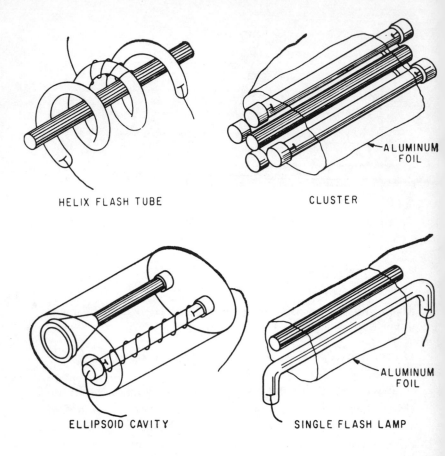

HELIX FLASH TUBE

CLUSTER

ALUMINUM FOIL

ELLIPSOID CAVITY

SINGLE FLASH LAMP

ALUMINUM FOIL

Laser-head designs used in optical pumping of ruby crystals. Each design concentrates light emitted from flash lamps onto the ruby rod (*Electronics*)

the whole business in aluminum foil as if you were going to barbecue an ear of corn. The baked-in-foil arrangement has the added charm that the foil can be used as the trigger electrode (more about this later). Remember, though, that since the foil can get hot and since the trigger electrode has a voltage on it as high as that on the picture tube of a TV set, the assembly must rest on a surface that is at once both heat-resistant and an excellent electrical insulator. Something like Pyroceram should do nicely.

ELLIPSOID REFLECTOR

Scientists have found, however, that the amount of power that needs be delivered to the flash lamps before a laser will fire can be drastically reduced, perhaps by a factor of ten, by careful design of the reflector surrounding the laser-rod and flash-lamp assembly.

Several researchers have found that an ellipsoid reflector gives the best results. Here the reflector has an elliptical instead of a round cross section. It is used with a single linear flash lamp. The axis or center line of the flash lamp is clamped at one focus of the ellipse, while the center line of the ruby rod is clamped at the other focus. This geometrical arrangement takes advantage of a basic mathematical property of the ellipse: namely, that all light rays leaving the lamp at one focus will be directed into the ruby rod at the other focus.

U-SHAPED LAMPS

There are U-shaped flash lamps available, as well as helical or straight lamps. And all flash tubes are available in a number of different power ratings. The U-shaped lamps are used in the same way as straight lamps, but the lamps are somewhat easier to handle and mount because the connections to the lamp are out of the way of the ruby rod. For example, if a ruby rod and flash lamp are wrapped in an aluminum foil reflector and if the aluminum foil is used as the trigger electrode to fire the lamp, the clamps can be attached to the sides of the U-shaped lamp well away from the high-potential aluminum foil.

The General Electric Photo Lamp Department, Nela Park, Cleveland, Ohio, publishes a comprehensive manual covering several types of flash tubes. It includes details on power-supply requirements and design as well as flash-lamp operation. The same company also publishes a data sheet describing the construction of a simple laser.

Designing the Power Supply

The next step in the construction of a simple ruby laser is to design a power supply to energize the laser through the flashtube. Actually, the threshold level, the energy level at which the laser will begin to emit coherent light, will determine the rating of the flashtube itself.

ENERGY REQUIREMENTS

Today most off-the-shelf ruby rods will display laser action at threshold levels around 150 joules if an efficient reflector system is used. Maiman's first successful laser required a pump energy of over 2,400 joules.

All things being equal, the pumping energy needed by a laser varies as the diameter of the laser rod varies: the thicker the rod, the more pump energy required to fire it. A laser rod ony one-tenth of an inch thick was found to have a threshold level of less than 100 joules.

Actually, to get the maximum possible energy output in the laser beam itself a laser may be operated at two to four times threshold energy level. Remember that the ruby laser is a notoriously inefficient device, and so in a typical device only about one-tenth of one percent of the pumping energy will be turned into coherent light output.

One of the first laser power supplies marketed was rated at 780 joules and sold for $1,500. Today laser power supplies of 800, 2,000 joules or more are available. An 800-joule supply can be obtained for $400 to $500. By the same token, early laser heads sold for $1,000, while today a whole laser capable of putting out one joule of coherent light can be obtained for about $950.

You can build an 800-joule power supply for about $300.

To give you an idea of the size of laser power supplies: a commercial power supply delivering up to 800 joules uses a 2,000-volt power supply and a 400-microfarad capacitor bank. (A capacitor is an electrical part that stores charge in a layer of dielectric material sandwiched between two conducting plates. A capacitor bank is a group of several interconnected capacitors.) The power supply stands nearly four feet high. It is 2 feet wide, 20 inches deep, and weighs over 300 pounds.

A 2,000-joule power supply also uses a 2,000-volt power supply but has a 1,000-microfarad capacitor bank. It is the same size as the 800-joule power supply, but weighs one hundred pounds more!

HOW THE POWER SUPPLY WORKS

In general there are two parts to a laser power supply. One part is the main or variable-frequency high-voltage supply. This can be described as a half-wave power supply. It plugs into a 110-volt, 60-cycle alternating-current supply and converts it to pulsating direct current whose voltage may be varied from 0 to 2,000 volts.

The main supply charges up a bank of large capacitors, storers of electrical energy, through a resistor. The flash-tube is connected across the terminals of the capacitor bank. A voltmeter is also connected across the capacitor bank. The voltmeter is used to tell when the capacitor bank has charged up enough to fire the laser. This value is usually taken nominally as one half the voltage delivered by the half-wave power supply.

The second part of the laser power supply is called the trigger power supply. It may be any kind of direct-current power supply capable of putting out around 400 volts of direct-current power when plugged into an alternating-

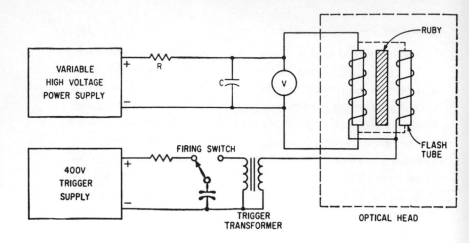

Typical laser system. High-voltage supply can be a simple trans-
former-rectifier that trickle charges the capacitor bank *(Electronics)*

current line. The trigger power supply charges up another
capacitor—a relatively small one of 8 or 12 microfarads will
do. The capacitor is connected to the trigger power supply
as long as the firing switch is in its open or de-energized
position.

When the firing switch or trigger is depressed or closed,
the trigger capacitor is connected to the primary or input
side of a high-voltage trigger transformer. These transformers usually have about a 40-to-1 step-up ratio; in other
words, a 400-volt pulse across the primary develops a 16-
kilovolt pulse across the secondary. One side of the secondary is tied internally to one side of the primary. The
remaining free end of the secondary winding (or output
side of the high-voltage transformer) is wound around the
flashtubes.

When the firing key is depressed, the trigger capacitor
discharges about 400 volts through the primary winding
(actually, the trigger capacitor seldom gets a chance to

charge up to the full 400 volts) and develops a pulse of about 15,000 volts across the secondary windings of the trigger transformer.

As this pulse races through the wires wound around the flash lamps, it sets up an electromagnetic field that ionizes some of the xenon gas molecules in the flashtubes. This creates electrons and positive ions and renders the xenon gas electrically conducting.

When the xenon gas becomes conductive, the electrons that have piled up on the negative side of the main capacitor bank surge through the flashtubes on their way to the positive side of the capacitor bank. This action fires the xenon flash lamps which irradiate the laser rod with a brilliant blue-green flash of visible light.

Now we must determine the power requirements of the laser and decide upon the size of the main capacitor bank.

Energy measures the intensity of the laser pump. To convert energy values to pulse power, we have to divide the energy of the pumping light pulse by the duration of the pumping pulse.

Thus if an 800-joule supply puts out a pulse five-thousandths of a second long, it may be said to have a peak pulse power of 160,000 watts. But if the charging time of the capacitor bank is, say, 15 seconds, then only four pulses are delivered each minute, and the average power of the pump is only about 53 watts.

For the mathematically inclined:

$$\text{Peak pulse power} = \frac{\text{energy}}{\text{pulse width}} =$$

$$\frac{800 \text{ joules}}{0.005 \text{ second}} = 160,000 \text{ watts}$$

And:

$$\text{Average power} = \text{peak pulse power} \times \frac{\text{pulse width}}{\text{pulse period}} =$$
$$160{,}000 \text{ watts} \times \frac{0.005 \text{ seconds}}{15 \text{ seconds}} = 53 \text{ watts}$$

Therefore our laser will consume only about as much electricity as a medium-sized light bulb!

CHOOSING THE CAPACITOR

The electrical charge (in coulombs) stored in a capacitor is equal to the electrical size of the capacitor given in farads multiplied by the voltage across the capacitor in volts. However, we can't count the whole 2,000 volts of our main power supply as being used to charge up our capacitor bank.

Remember, there is a resistor connected between the capacitor bank and the main power supply. Now, the product of the electrical size of the capacitor in farads and the electrical size of this resistor in ohms is known as the time constant of the capacitor-charging circuit. It is expressed, strangely enough, in seconds.

If the capacitor were connected across the terminals of the 2,000-volt power supply for an extremely long period of time, enough electrons would flow into the capacitor so that when the power supply was disconnected and replaced by a voltmeter, the voltmeter would indicate 2,000 volts. But if the power supply is connected to the capacitor terminals for only a period of time equal to $R \times C$ seconds (the value of the time constant), the capacitor will charge up to about two-thirds of the total power-supply voltage. Then when the power supply is disconnected and replaced by a voltmeter, the voltmeter will read about 1,240 volts. However, in laser work, the capacitor bank is usually considered to be charged enough when the voltmeter reads one-half the output of the main power supply, or 1,000 volts.

Under these conditions, the charge on the capacitor will be given by:

$$\text{Charge in coulombs} = \text{capacitor size in farads} \times \text{voltage in volts}$$

But when the flashtube is ionized, the capacitor discharges through the tube. Now, the energy of this discharge is measured in joules, or, as we have said earlier, in coulomb-volts:

$$\text{Energy in joules} = \text{capacitor charge in coulombs} \times \text{power-supply voltage in volts}$$

Now we have all the information necessary to design a laser pump supply.

Suppose we want to build a one-joule laser. We assume that our reflector system will produce a laser that is about one-tenth of one percent efficient ($0.1\% = 0.001$). Therefore the optical pump must supply

$$\frac{\text{one joule}}{0.001} = 1,000 \text{ joules}$$

Now let's find out how much charge we must have on our capacitor to deliver this much optical pumping energy with a 2,000-volt main power supply. This is given by:

$$\text{Charge in coulombs} = \frac{\text{energy in joules}}{\text{supply voltage in volts}} =$$

$$\frac{1,000}{2,000} = \frac{1}{2} \text{ coulomb}$$

In order to get a charge of one-half coulomb with a 2,000-volt power supply that is allowed to charge the capacitor to only 1,000 volts, we need a capacitor whose size is given by

$$\text{Capacitor size in farads} = \frac{\text{charge in coulombs}}{\text{voltage in volts}} =$$
$$\frac{0.5}{1,000} = 0.0005 \text{ farad}$$

Since the farad is such an ungainly unit, engineers work with a smaller unit called the microfarad, or one-millionth farad. Therefore, to fire our flash lamps we need a 500-microfarad capacitor bank.

Now, a 500-microfarad capacitor is a big piece of hardware. The capacitors used in laser work are certainly not lightweight units; they are usually heavy-duty, oil-filled devices designed for rugged use.

Suppose only 20-microfarad units are available, how do we get our 500-microfarad bank? By hooking up 25 of our 20-microfarad capacitors in parallel—that is, with all the positive terminals of the capacitors connected together and hence to the positive terminal of the main power supply, and all the negative terminals of the capacitors connected together and hence to the negative terminal of the power supply.

TIME BETWEEN PULSES

Then how about the time between laser pulses? This depends upon the $R \times C$ time constant of the capacitor charging circuit which in turn depends upon the value of the resistor in series with the capacitor:

$$\text{Time constant in seconds} = \text{resistance in ohms} \times$$
$$\text{capacitance in farads}$$

Or for a 15-second charging time and a 500-microfarad capacitor bank:

$$\text{Size of resistor in ohms} =$$
$$\frac{\text{time constant in seconds}}{\text{size of capacitor in farads}} = \frac{15}{0.0005} = 30,000 \text{ ohms}$$

LENGTH OF THE PULSE

The next question to be resolved is the length of the laser pulse. When engineers talk about the length of these pulses, even the second becomes an ungainly unit with which to measure time. So they talk about microseconds.

It turns out that it takes about 400 microseconds, or 0.0004 second, before the ruby rod begins to emit coherent light. And suppose we want a laser pulse five thousandths of a second long. This means the ruby rod must be pumped above threshold for at least 5,000 microseconds after the rod begins to lase.

Thus, the optical pumping pulse from the flash lamp must last at least 5,400 microseconds at a sufficient energy level to keep the laser emitting coherent light for the length of the desired pulse.

The optical pumping circuit we have been talking about would not quite accomplish this. A capacitor, it turns out, discharges to about 38 percent of its peak charge in the length of our old friend the RC or resistor-capacitor time constant.

This was, you recall, found by multiplying the electrical size or value of the capacitor in farads by the value of resistance in the circuit in ohms. However, the 33,000-ohm charging resistor is not part of the circuit after the flash lamp fires. Now the only resistance of any consequence is the resistance of the plasma or ionized gas in the flashtube. This resistance ranges from 80 to 120 ohms, depending upon the flash lamp used.

This circuit gives a time constant of 0.0005 farad $\times$ 100 ohms = 50,000 microseconds. In 0.05 seconds, therefore, the charge across the capacitor will fall to 38 percent of its peak value. In one-tenth of the time-constant period it will fall to 90 percent of its peak value. However, the largest amount of energy will be delivered at the start of the pulse before the ruby rod starts to lase, and not when it is really needed, even though the length of time of the desired pulse is nearly within limits (that is, within one-tenth of the time-constant period).

A resistor-capacitor circuit charges up like an ordinary hill but discharges like a ski slope!

However, there is a way to straighten out this ski slope, and that is by use of another kind of time constant called the inductor-resistor or L/R time constant. This time constant applies to a circuit with a resistor (in the laser, the ionized gas column in the flashtube) and an inductor (a coil of wire also called a choke).

In such a circuit, the pulse builds up slowly like the charging hill of the capacitor. It builds up to 62 percent of its peak value in the period of the time constant. Suppose we connect a 0.5 millihenry inductor between the capacitor and the flashtube. (The henry is a measure of the electrical size or value of an inductor. Like the farad, by which the value of a capacitor is measured, the henry is an ungainly unit. Sizes of practical inductors are usually given in millihenrys, or thousandths of henry.) The L/R time constant is given by

$$\frac{\text{value of inductance in henrys}}{\text{value of resistance in ohms}} =$$

$$\frac{0.005}{100} = 5 \text{ microseconds}$$

This isn't very long, but it does temper the ski-slope discharge curve of the capacitor bank enough so the laser can get started before the real surge of the optical pump has dissipated itself.

So far, we have covered the high points of the construction of a ruby laser: the ruby rod, the reflector, flashtube with its main and triggering supplies. But we have not discussed the design of the variable high-voltage power supply or the lower-voltage trigger power supply.

MORE ABOUT POWER SUPPLIES

These are two of the most elementary electronic circuits. For the variable high-voltage supply you need a 1-to-1 transformer with a variable tap on the secondary or output side. This will enable you to vary the input to the following high-voltage transformer from 0 to the full 110 volts available from the alternating-current power lines.

The high-voltage transformer will have about a 15-to-1 step-up ratio. One of the secondary leads must go to the anode of your rectifier and one to the cathode. The rectifier may be either a type 2 X 2 high-vacuum electron tube or a multiple-series stack of silicon diodes. To be on the safe side, the stack should be rated for 2,500 to 3,000 volts. If you are going to use a vacuum tube, you will need a ceramic tube socket in which to mount it and you will have to select a high-voltage transformer that incorporates a two-volt filament winding to heat the filaments of the 2 X 2 vacuum tube. The silicon rectifier stack needs no socket or filament supply. The stacks usually come complete with their own hardware for mounting right on your chassis.

TRIGGER SUPPLY

The trigger power supply requires only a 4-to-1 step-up transformer. The primary windings connect to the 110-volt alternating-current power line, while the two leads from the secondary winding connect to the anode and cathode of your rectifier. You can use a single silicon or selenium rectifier rated for, say, 600 volts, or a high-vacuum rectifier such as a 5U4G with its two plates and two cathodes tied together.

As with the high-voltage supply, the vacuum tube requires a socket that can be phenolic instead of ceramic, and you will have to select a power transformer with a 5-volt filament winding to heat the filaments of the 5U4G. The silicon rectifier usually has its own hardware; in fact, it may have a stud cathode that screws right into your chassis.

Because one side of the firing switch or key is 400 volts hot, it is advisable for safety to use a pushbutton Microswitch.

SAFETY FEATURES

Commercial laser power supplies have fairly elaborate safety features. They have interlocked doors. An interlock is a plug that disconnects to disable the power supply when you open the doors of the cabinet surrounding it.

These commercial units have two separate red indicator lamps that tell when the high-voltage and trigger power supplies are energized. There are also separate line switches to turn the power supplies on and off. The trigger transformer that converts our 400 volts to 15,000 volts for triggering the xenon tube is usually located in or on the laser housing itself. This is also called the laser head. A coaxial cable connects the laser housing or head to the power supply.

Most power supplies have incorporated a heavy-duty relay that bleeds the charge off the capacitor bank when the power is turned off. This prevents accidental firing of the laser.

Modern small laser and a portable power supply (Raytheon)

Remember, however, even though a laser is inherently no more dangerous than a television receiver, the voltages it uses are dangerous to life. A typical laser power supply uses 15,000 volts for the trigger, 2,000 volts for the main supply, and 400 volts to supply the trigger transformer—and an electric chair uses only 2,000 volts!

Manufacturers do all they can to make equipment safe, but no equipment can ever be made foolproof for fools. A bleed-off relay can get stuck, and a laser can still fire accidentally. So if you value your eyes, never look down the barrel of a laser whether the power switch is on or off. Furthermore, interlocks can be shorted or intentionally by-passed, and indicator lamps can burn out. Therefore, just as you should treat every gun as if it were loaded, treat every high-voltage power supply as if it were hot (energized) until you make sure it really is turned off.

On the west coast, Hughes Aircraft in Culver City, California, among others, sells laser heads and laser power supplies. On the east coast, Raytheon's Special Microwave Devices Operation in Waltham, Massachusetts, sells laser heads and laser power supplies as well as ruby rods. Edgerton, Germeshausen and Grier of Boston, Massachusetts, sells flash lamps, reflector systems, and power supplies.

IS THE LASER WORKING?

Suppose that now you have built, bought, begged, or borrowed a laser complete with flashtube, reflector, and two power supplies. How do you know that the laser is really lasing? It could just be fluorescing, and in this case you might just as well have made a fluorescent lamp. Before the laser is entered into the high school science fair, you'd better make sure you are really getting coherent light out of it.

There are many complicated ways to determine this, but with a ruby laser the easiest way is to look at the spot the laser beam makes on a wall.

Watch the spot on the wall and increase the output of the variable high-voltage power supply. See if you can narrow the red area down to a tiny spot by increasing the voltage.

Ruby fluorescence gives a broad, diffuse beam that looks dull red. Look for a brilliant tiny flash of deep crimson light. But remember that all the output of a laser is not coherent, so don't be dismayed if the tiny flash of brilliant crimson light is surrounded by a broad, diffuse halo of dull-red incoherent light. It is the tiny spot in the center that makes the big difference. Look for it. If you have it, you have made a laser.

CONCLUSION

This is the end of a book, but the real story of the laser is only beginning.

Despite the carnival showmanship and the debunking that have marked the laser's first three years of existence, its discovery ranks in its potential impact on technology along with De Forest's Audion tube and Shockley's transistor. Not only can the laser reshape the field of electronics, it can also have a profound and far-reaching effect on every phase of scientific endeavor.

At this instant, momentous discoveries in the field of medicine are almost ready to be announced—not only the laser's actual use as a photocoagulator in retinal surgery of the human eye but also its effectiveness in destruction of malignant cells, elimination of growths and blemishes of the skin without danger of infection, and even its potential use in stomach surgery and in dentistry.

And scientists and engineers are approaching the laser with more respect and caution these days. Several laboratories are enforcing elaborate safety precautions. It has been found that reflected light from high-powered lasers may be harmful to human vision: at present, there are five known cases of laser damage to the eye; three victims have recovered, and one is well along the way, but the fifth may have sustained permanent injury. The laser is nothing to fool around with.

The laser is moving to new frontiers; and its quantum-mechanical cousin the maser has suddenly become more useful. Masers had enjoyed only limited use largely because of the bulky electromagnets needed to make them work. Now a new cryogenic electromagnet has been developed in which current that has started flowing in a wire cooled nearly to absolute zero keeps flowing and maintains its magnetic field almost indefinitely without any need for power. Now electromagnetic reconnaissance satellites searching for possible violations of the nuclear test ban treaty or other potential threats to world peace may soon have quantum-mechanical "ears" far more sensitive than any electron-tube or transistor amplifier.

This ends my brief introduction to a fascinating and unbelievably useful invention. The rest of the Story of the Laser may be yours to write in plants and laboratories throughout this nation and the world.

BIBLIOGRAPHY

Addeo, E. "Lasers Fill Medical Need," *Electronics* (April 19, 1963), p. 30.
"Are Masers Going Out of Style?" *Electronics* (February 8, 1963), p. 26.

Barnes, F. S., and D. Maley. "Beam Maser for 3 Millimeters Uses Hydrogen Cyanide," *Electronics* (March 17, 1961), p. 45.
Berland, T. *The Scientific Life*, in press.
"Biological Use for Lasers Reported at Meeting," *Electronics* (May 17, 1963), p. 60.
Burgess, J. Q. "New Concepts in Detecting Weak Electromagnetic Signals," *Electronics* (September 15, 1961), p. 49.
Burns, G., R. A. Loff, S. E. Blum, F. H. Dill, Jr., and M. J. Nathan. "Directionality Effects of GaAs Light-Emitting Diodes," *IBM Journal of Research and Development* (January, 1963), p. 62.
Bushor, W. E. "Sun and Exploding Wires Pump Lasers," *Electronics* (March 30, 1962), p. 24.

Carroll, J. M. *Careers and Opportunities in Electronics*. New York: E. P. Dutton & Co., Inc., 1963.
———. *Electron Devices and Circuits*. New York: McGraw-Hill Book Co., Inc., 1962.
Cedarholm, J. P., and C. H. Townes. "A New Experimental Test of Special Relativity," *Nature* (October 31, 1959), p. 1350.
"Cesium Gas C-W Laser Is Optically Pumped," *Electronics* (April 27, 1962), p. 23.
"Chromium Dopes C-W Laser's Ruby Crystal," *Electronics* (February 9, 1962), p. 30.
Ciftan, M., C. F. Luck, C. G. Shafer, and H. Statz. "A Ruby Laser with an Elliptic Configuration," *Proceedings of the Institute of Radio Engineers* (May, 1961).
Coblenz, A., and H. L. Owens. "Transistors: Theory and Application, Part II," *Electronics* (April, 1953), p. 138.
"Crystal Laser Puts Out Continuous Power," *Electronics* (January 12, 1962), p. 26.

"Diode Laser Transmits Audio," *Electronics* (May 31, 1963), p. 16.

"Diode Lasers to Accelerate Optical Communications," *Electronics* (November 16, 1962), p. 24.

Dirac, P. A. M. "The Evolution of the Physicist's Picture of Nature," *Scientific American* (May, 1963), p. 45.

Dulberger, L. H. "How Dangerous Are Lasers?" *Electronics* (January 26, 1962), p. 27.

———. "Will the Laser Succeed Sonar for Undersea Electronics?" *Electronics* (June 9, 1961), p. 24.

———. "Will Lasers Protect Our Cities Against ICBM's?" *Electronics* (May 3, 1963), p. 20.

Dulberger, L. H., and S. Vogel. "Lasers: Devices and Systems— Part II," *Electronics* (November 3, 1961), p. 40.

———. "Lasers: Devices and Systems—Part IV," *Electronics* (November 24, 1961), p. 54.

Dunlap, K. W., and D. L. Williams. "Will Lasers Weld Circuit Components?" *Electronics* (July 12, 1963), p. 54.

"Electronics Newsletter," *Electronics* (November 30, December 7, 14, 28, 1962; January 4, 11, 25, February 8, 15, 22, March 1, 8, 15, 22, 29, April 5, 12, 19, May 10, 17, 24, 31, June 7, 14, 21, 28, July 19, August 2, 9, 1963).

Erikson, A. "What's New in Lasers? Liquids, Intermetallics, Rare Earths," *Electronics* (March 1, 1963), p. 14.

Fontana, J. R., R. H. Pantell, and R. G. Smith. "Nonlinear Effects in Quantized Microwave Systems," *Electronics* (May 11, 1962), p. 79.

"Giant Ruby Laser Produces Harmonics," *Electronics* (May 10, 1963), p. 60.

Hall, R. N., G. E. Fenner, J. D. Kingsley, T. J. Soltys, and R. O. Carlson. "Coherent Light Emission from GaAs Junctions," *Physical Review Letters* (November 1, 1962).

Hausmann, E., and E. P. Slack. *Physics.* New York: D. Van Nostrand Co., Inc., 1939.

Heitler, W. *The Quantum Theory of Radiation.* 3rd ed. New York: Oxford University Press, 1954.

Holonyak, N., Jr. "First Color Photos Show Active Region in Visible-Light Diode Laser," *Electronics* (March 1, 1963), p. 35.

Hutter, R. G. E. "The Microwave Phototube: New Detector for Optical Receivers," *Electronics* (July 20, 1962), p. 37.

Jacobs, S. "The Optical Heterodyne—Key to Advanced Space Signaling," *Electronics* (July 12, 1963), p. 29.

Jaffe, B. *Michelson and the Speed of Light*. New York: Doubleday and Co., Inc., 1960.

Javan, A., W. R. Bennett, Jr., and D. R. Herriott. "Population Inversion and Continuous Optical Maser Action in a Gas Discharge Containing a He-Ne Mixture," *Physical Review Letters* (February, 1961), p. 106.

Jelley, J. V. "The Potentialities and Present Status of Masers and Parametric Amplifiers in Radio Astronomy," *Proceedings of the Institute of Electrical and Electronics Engineers* (January, 1963), p. 30.

Justice, B. "Boy Builds Advanced Science Unit," *Fort Worth Star Telegram* (March 24, 1963).

Kassel, S. "Soviet Laser Research," *Proceedings of the Institute of Electrical and Electronics Engineers* (January, 1963), p. 216.

"Kerr-Effect Readout Uses Gas Laser," *Electronics* (April 5, 1963), p. 48.

Kornberg, W. "Nonlinear Effects Convert Laser Beam, Amplify Light," *Electronics* (May 3, 1963), p. 30.

"Laser Advances," *Student Quarterly and Electrical Engineering Digest* (January, 1963), p. 26.

"Laser Beam Zips Through Diamonds," *Rensselaer Engineer* (January, 1963), p. 44.

"Laser Gyro's New Configurations," *Electronics* (June 28, 1963), p. 82.

"Laser Link in Gemini?" *Electronics* (June 14, 1963), p. 54.

"Laser Meetings Double Up," *Electronics* (April 12, 1963), p. 22.

"Laser Operates at Atmospheric Window," *Electronics* (May 18, 1962), p. 21.

"Laser Space Weapon in R&D," *Electronics* (December 22, 1961), p. 17.

"Laser's Future: Bright or Cloudy?" *Electronics* (March 2, 1962), p. 22.

"Lasers: State of the Art," *Electronic Progress* (January–February, 1963).

Lehr, C. G. "The Generation of Coherent Light," *Student Quarterly and Electrical Engineering Digest* (September, 1962), p. 2.

"Liquid Laser Emits Visible Light," *Electronics* (March 8, 1963), p. 27.

Lock, C., R. Paananen, and H. Statz. *Design of a Gaseous Optical Maser*. Boston: Raytheon Co., August 14, 1961.

Luck, C. F., Jr. "Optical Masers," *Electronic Progress* (July–August, 1961), p. 9.

Maguire, T. "Air Force Research Aim: Detection Capabilities," *Electronics* (April 26, 1963), p. 72.
———. "Laser Used to Confirm Physical Standards," *Electronics* (March 22, 1963), p. 74.
———. "Microwelding: Laser or Electron Beam?" *Electronics* (July 5, 1963), p. 23.
Maiman, T. H. "Stimulated Optical Radiation in Ruby Masers," *Nature* (August, 1960), p. 493.
Mendenhall, C. E., A. S. Eve, D. A. Keys, and R. M. Sutton. *College Physics*. Boston: D. C. Heath and Co., 1944.
Meyer, J. W. "The Solid-State Maser—A Supercooled Amplifier," *Electronics* (April 25, 1958), p. 66.
———. "Systems Applications of Solid-State Masers," *Electronics* (November 4, 1960), p. 58.
Michel, A. E., E. J. Walker, and M. J. Nathan. "Determination of the Active Region in Light-Emitting GaAs Diodes," *IBM Journal* (January, 1963), p. 70.
Miller, B. "Aerospace Military Laser Uses Explored," *Aviation Week & Space Technology* (April 22, 1963), p. 54.

"Now Lasers Are Industrial Tools," *Electronics* (March 29, 1963), p. 16.

"Off-the-Shelf Components for Optical Masers," *Electronics* (August 4, 1961), p. 62.
"Optical Techniques Can Raise Computer Speed," *Electronics* (November 9, 1962), p. 30.
"Organic Laser Research Project at Brooklyn Polytechnic Institute," *Electronics* (May 17, 1963), p. 58.

Principles and Applications of Lasers. Boston: Raytheon Co., May 8, 1962.

Schawlow, A. L. "Optical Masers," *Scientific American* (June, 1961).
Schawlow, A. L. and C. H. Townes. "Infrared and Optical Masers," *Physical Review* (December, 1958), p. 1940.
"Servo Controls Helium-Neon Gas Laser Output," *Electronics* (March 8, 1963), p. 58.
Solomon, L. "Doppler Laser Measures Speeds Down to 0.00004 MPH," *Electronics* (July 20, 1962), p. 26.

Soltes, A. S. "Military Potential of Lasers," *The Military Engineer* (November–December, 1962), p. 416.

"Special Report: The Laser—Light Amplification by Stimulated Emission of Radiation," *Business Week* (August 18, 1962).

"Stanford Reveals Progress in Laser Communications and Neuron Memories," *Electronics* (September 15, 1961), p. 20.

Stitch, N. L., E. J. Woodbury, and J. H. Morse. "Optical Ranging System Uses Laser Transmitter," *Electronics* (April 21, 1961), p. 51.

Tippett, J. T., and H. E. Puthoff. "Optical Computers Approach Reality," *Electronics* (May 3, 1963), p. 72.

Tomaino, M. F. "Chelate Lasers Are Coming on Strong," *Electronics* (April 26, 1963), p. 32.

Townes, C. H. "Masers," in *The Age of Electronics*. Ed. C. Overhage. New York: McGraw-Hill Book Co., Inc., 1962.

———. "Some Applications of Optical and Infrared Masers," in *Advances in Quantum Electronics*. Ed. J. Singer. New York: Columbia University Press, 1961.

"Try Laser for Plasma Density Measurements," *Electronics* (April 27, 1962), p. 34.

"Try for Triode Lasers," *Electronics* (May 24, 1963), p. 32.

"Undersea Coherent Light," *Electronics* (February 22, 1963), p. 30.

Vali, V., and W. Vali. "Induced Gamma-Ray Emission," *Proceedings of the Institute of Electrical and Electronics Engineers* (January, 1963), p. 182.

Vogel, S. "High-Frequency Optical Phonon Masing Reported," *Electronics* (January 4, 1963), p. 102.

Vogel, S., and L. H. Dulberger. "Lasers: Devices and Systems—Part I," *Electronics* (October 27, 1961), p. 39.

———. "Lasers: Devices and Systems—Part II," *Electronics* (November 10, 1961), p. 81.

Weber, S. "Laser Beam Carries TV Video and Audio," *Electronics* (February 22, 1963), p. 23.

Wiley, C. M. "Technical Preview of Next Week's National Electronics Conference," *Electronics* (October 5, 1962), p. 39.

"Will Lasers Settle Down?" *Electronics* (April 5, 1963), p. 24.

Wolff, M. F. "Air Force Outlines Latest R&D Plans," *Electronics* (May 24, 1963), p. 16.

———. "Field Modulates Laser," *Electronics* (April 26, 1963), p. 26.

———. "Frequency Control Lags SSB," *Electronics* (June 7, 1963), p. 16.

———. "Look at What Optical Semiconductors Do Now," *Electronics* (June 28, 1963), p. 32.

———. "Need a New Laser Frequency? Single Noble Gas Gives 14 More," *Electronics* (August 17, 1962), p. 28.

———. "New Laser Structure Drives Output Past 1 W," *Electronics* (June 21, 1963), p. 24.

"X-Band Microwave Laser Demodulator," *Electronics* (April 5, 1963), p. 50.

Yariv, A., and J. P. Gordon. "The Laser, *Proceedings of the Institute of Electrical and Electronics Engineers* (January, 1963), p. 4.

INDEX

accelerometers, 127
actinide elements, 36
adaptive logic, 137
Air Force, 76
"Albacore" hull, 114
aluminum oxide, 29
ammonia-beam maser, 80
ammonia molecule, 78
ammonium dihydrogen phosphate, 117
analog computers, 133
angstrom units, 22
angular velocity, 128
antennas, 63
antilaser countermeasures, 110
antimissile laser, 106
antimissile missiles, 105
antimissile weapons, 51
antipersonnel lasers, 120
antisubmarine warfare, 48, 114
Arecibo radio telescope, 88
Armstrong, Robert, 146
atomic orbits, 27, 30, 69
average power, 160
azimuthal momenta, 30

Ballistic Missile Early Warning System, 105
Balmer, Johann, 69
Basov, N. G., 73
Bell Telephone Laboratories, 75, 84, 87, 97, 98
Bennett, William R., 97
biological effects, 141
black-body problem, 63
bleed-off relay, 166
blinding, 142
Bloembergen, Nicolaas, 82, 87
blue-green lasers, 48, 117
Bohr, Niels, 69
bolometer, 64

cancer surgery, 144
capacitor bank, 162
capacitors, 157
charging time, 162
chelate lasers, 47, 136
chemical pumping, 110, 120
chromium ions, 46
chromium oxide, 29
coherence, 19, 168
Columbia University, 76
computers, 51-52, 133
continuous-wave lasers, 35
cosmic rays, 23
cryogenic temperatures, 35
cryostat, 42
crystal growth, 149

dangers of a laser, 146
"dead-man" switch, 108
de Broglie, Louis, 71
dental uses, 56
dewar flask, 86
diffraction gratings, 132
diffusion masks, 53, 132
digital computers, 133
diodes, 39
divergence, of light rays, 35
doping, 36, 40
doppler laser radar, 124
dynamo, 60

Echo satellite, 90
economics, 9, 156
Edgerton, Germeshausen and Grier, 168
Einstein, Albert, 67, 71
electromagnetic spectrum, 21
electromagnetic waves, 21
electrons, 40
electron spin, 30, 81
ellipsoid reflector, 155

emission spectrum, 69
energy, 23, 159, 161
energy absorption, 76
energy levels, 30
energy states, 24, 30
Eniac computer, 137
ether drift, 57
extragalactic communications, 144
eye surgery, 142

Fabrikant, V. A., 72
Fabry-Perot interferometer, 37
Faraday, Michael, 60
Feher, G., 84
fiber optics, 50, 134
fine grinding, 151
firing switch, 158
flash-lamp cluster, 153
flash lamps, 152
flashtubes, 30
fluorescence, 24
fluorescent lamps, 25
forward biasing, 40
frauds, 58
frequency, 21
frequency coherence, 25
frequency doubling, 119
frequency mixing, 27
frequency multiplication, 27
fusing circuits, 107
fusion reaction, 106

gallium-arsenide diodes, 45, 98
gallium-arsenide lasers, 40
gallium-arsenide-phosphide lasers, 42
gamma-ray lasers, 48
gamma rays, 23
gaseous lasers, 43, 97; electrically pumped, 36; optically pumped, 38
gasers, 45
Gatling-gun laser, 110
General Electric, 98, 155
general heating effect, 141
General Telephone and Electronics, 98
glass lasers, 36
Gordon, James P., 79

Hall, Robert N., 98
Harvard University, 82
H-bomb, effects on radio, 90
Heisenberg, Werner, 70
Heitler, Walter, 72
helical flash lamp, 152
helium-neon lasers, 37, 97
Herriott, D. R., 97
Hertz, Heinrich Rudolph, 61, 67
holes, 40
hydrogen laser, 112
hydrophones, 116
horsepower, 111
Hughes Aircraft, 168
Hughes Research Laboratories, 95

identification-friend-or-foe, 109
induced emission, 72
inductor, 164
inertial guidance, 127
inertial platform, 127
infrared, 22, 38
infrared communications, 52, 98, 120
infrared lasers, 47
injection lasers, 39, 44, 98
integrators, 128
intensity, 24
interferometers, 37
interlocks, 166
International Business Machines, 98
ionosphere, 90
irasers, 45

Jansky, Karl, 87
Javan, Ali, 97
joule, 111

kinetic energy, 24

laser: acronym, 17; prediction of, 94; invention of, 96
laser altimeters, 51
laser gyroscopes, 126
laser radar, 123
laser range finders, 52, 121
laser side arms, 120

laser surgery, 56
light pipes, 55, 140
light, speed of, 21
Lincoln Laboratory, 80, 84, 89
Linde Air Products, 151
linear flash lamps, 153
liquid lasers, 36
L/R time constant, 164
lunar excursion module, 125
Lyman, Theodore, 69

machining, 53, 130
Maiman, Theodore H., 95
main capacitor, 160
main power supply, 157, 165
maser, acronym, 17
masers, 46, 72, 80
matrix mechanics, 70
Maxwell, James Clerk, 60
McWhorter, Alan L., 84
measurement, 56
medical uses, 55
metal burning, 111
metastable states, 31, 38
Meyer, James W., 85
Michaelson-Morley experiment, 57
microcircuits, 131
microelectronic circuits, 53
microwave computers, 134
microwave modulation, 50
microwave phototube, 139
microwave pumping, 46, 84
microwave spectroscopy, 76
microwelding, 130
Millstone Hill radar, 87
Minuteman missile, 106
missile decoys, 108
modulation, 26
molecular amplifiers, 18, 80
molecular-beam clocks, 81
molecular beams, 77
monochromatic light, 27
Mount Palomar telescope, 88
multiplex communications, 54
multiplexing, 50

Nancy equipment, 52
Nathan, Marshall I., 98
negative absorption, 79

neodymium-glass laser, 119
neon lights, 25
Nerst tubes, 52
New York University, 120
Nike X, 108
Nike Zeus, 108
N-region, 40
nuclear fission, 107
nuclear submarines, 114

Oersted, Hans Christian, 60
Office of Naval Research, 77
optical computers, 137
optically pumped lasers, 44
optical masers, 18
optical pumping, 35
optical radar, 106, 109
orbital shifts, 27, 30
orbiting space stations, 105

parallel rays, 35
paramagnetic materials, 81
Paschen, Friedrich, 69
peak pulse power, 159
Perkin-Elmer Corp., 152
phosphors, 24
photography, 53, 132
photons, 30
photon theory, 68
Planck, Max, 66
Planck's constant, 23, 67
plasma sheath, 126
plastic lasers, 35, 136
Polar Ionosphere Satellite, 124
Polaris submarines, 128
polarization, 139
polishing, of ruby rods, 29
population inversion, 32, 79
potassium cobaltocyanide maser, 85
potassium dihydrogen phosphate, 117, 139
potential energy, 24
power, 159
power supply, 157
P-region, 40
process control, 54
Project Apollo, 125

Project Gemini, 124
Project Mercury, 126
Project Ozma, 144
Project Westford, 90
Prokhorov, A. M., 73
protective goggles, 142
pulsed lasers, 35
pulse length, 163

Q spoiling, 104
quantum, 23
quantum devices, 18
quantum jumps, 27
quantum mechanics, 18, 70

Rabi, Isidor I., 76
radar altimeter, 125
radar bombing, 75
radar speedmeters, 125
radiant energy, 20
radiation pressure, 113
radio astronomy, 47, 87
radio-frequency pumping, 37
radio telescopes, 88
radio waves, 62
Ramo, Simon, 75
rare-earth elements, 36
rasers, 45
rate gyroscope, 130
Raytheon Corp., 168
RC time constant, 160
recombination, 41
rectifiers, 165-66
Rediker, Robert H., 98
reflection, of photons, 32
repetition rate, 162
resonators, 77
retina surgery, 55
reverse biasing, 40
ruby boule, 149
ruby crystal, 149
ruby lasers, 28, 96, 103, 148
ruby, synthetic, 29

satellite communications, 47
Schawlow, Arthur L., 77, 92
Schliering photography, 132
Schrödinger, Erwin, 70
Scovil, H. E. D., 84

Seidel, H., 84
selective etching, 53
semiconductor junctions, 40
semiconductors, 39
shock wave, 113
Signal Corps, 80
silicon-carbide lasers, 43
silvering, of ruby rods, 29
smooth grinding, 151
solar furnaces, 103, 109
sonar, 115
space communications, 55, 124
space-tracking radar, 87
spatial coherence, 28
specific heating effect, 141
spectroscopy, 58
spectrum, 21
squibs, 107
stable table, 127
standing waves, 62
stimulated emission, 32, 39, 72
Stratoscope balloon, 113
subtraction, color, 29
Syncom satellites, 91

T-2 (Soviet) missile, 106
telephone transmission, 50
telephone trunking, 140
television, 138
television transmission, 50
Telstar satellites, 91
Texas Instruments, 98
thermal equilibrium, 71
three-level maser, 84
Tornadotron, 46
Townes, Charles H., 73, 91
tracking radar, 106
transducers, 115
transformers, 165
transistors, 130
transmissometers, 54
triangulation, 121
trigger capacitor, 158
trigger power supply, 157, 165
trigger transformer, 158

ultraviolet, 23
ultraviolet lasers, 48
underwater communications, 119

underwater laser, 116
underwater listening stations, 116
U-shaped flash lamp, 155
uvasers, 45

visible energy detection and ranging, 118
visible light, 22

wave equation, 71
wavelength, 21

wave mechanics, 71
Weber, Joseph, 72
welding, 53
Wooldridge, Dean, 75
work function, 68

xasers, 45
xenon flashtube, 30
X rays, 23

Zeiger, H. J., 79